SCIEN
MATTERS

Discovering the Deep Oceans

*prepared for the Course Team
by Angela Colling*

Science: a second level course

The S280 Course Team

Pam Berry (Text Processing)

Norman Cohen (Author)

Angela Colling (Author)

Michael Gillman (Author)

John Greenwood (Librarian)

Barbara Hodgson (Reader)

David Johnson (Author)

Carol Johnstone (Course Secretary)

Hilary MacQueen (Author)

Isla McTaggart (Course Manager)

Diane Mole (Designer)

Joanna Munnelly (Editor)

Pat Murphy (Author)

Ian Nuttall (Editor)

Pam Owen (Graphic Artist)

Malcolm Scott (Author)

Sandy Smith (Author)

Margaret Swithenby (Editor)

Jeff Thomas (Course Team Chair and Author)

Kiki Warr (Author)

Bill Young (BBC Producer)

External Assessor: John Durant

The Open University, Walton Hall, Milton Keynes MK7 6AA.

First published 1993. Reprinted 1995, 1996, 1998, 2002.

Copyright © 1993 The Open University.

Edited, designed and typeset in the United Kingdom by the Open University.

Printed in the United Kingdom by The Burlington Press, Foxton, Cambridge CB2 6SW.

ISBN 07492 51077

This text forms part of an Open University Second Level Course. If you have not enrolled on the course and would like to buy this or other Open University material, please write to Open University Educational Enterprises Ltd, 12 Cofferidge Close, Stony Stratford, Milton Keynes, MK11 1BY, United Kingdom. If you wish to enquire about enrolling as an Open University student please write to The Admissions Office, The Open University, PO Box 48, Walton Hall, Milton Keynes, MK7 6AB, United Kingdom.

1.4

11755C/s280ddoi1.4

Contents

I Introduction

There are 'frontiers of learning' in all fields of science, from genetics to geochemistry. In some cases, such frontiers are associated with frontiers of human experience— space, the hostile polar regions and, equally hostile to would-be investigators, the abyss of the deep sea.

Today politicians and planners are looking to the deep sea[*] for solutions to some of the most pressing problems of the modern world. They see it variously as a source of natural resources fast diminishing on land, as extra space in which to dump wastes, as a sink for greenhouse gases, and even as extra living space for an ever-growing human population. As a result, scientific research of the deep oceans has acquired a kind of urgency.

Until the 1860s almost nothing was known about the deep sea; indeed much of the received wisdom owed more to the imagination than to observation. The tremendous increase in knowledge and understanding of the past hundred years or so has not been the result of a gradual accumulation of facts, but more the outcome of a series of revolutions in thought. The aim of this book is to use one particular scientific problem, that of the existence of life in the deep sea, to look at how some of these revolutions came about and, sometimes (and perhaps more importantly), at what prevented them from occurring earlier.

Along the way you will encounter just a few of the thousands of people who, since the early nineteenth century, have tried to understand the deep oceans. Individual people are an important part of the story because, while beliefs may change, and society, technology and ideas develop, people remain essentially the same—and it is people who do science.

[*] Given the title of this book I should clarify what I mean by 'deep' and 'ocean'. By 'ocean' I mean water beyond the edge of the continental shelf, which is generally at a depth of 100–200 m (but can be as shallow as 50 m or as deep as 500 m); 'sea' is used interchangeably with 'ocean' and is only occasionally used to imply relatively shallow water, partly or wholly enclosed and overlying the continental shelf (such as the North Sea or the Aegean Sea). Conversely, 'deep' can be taken to mean deeper than a few hundred metres, and certainly deeper than the depth to which sunlight penetrates.

2 Clear, still and heavier than molten gold

As I looked out over the tossing oceans and at the sinking sun, and realized what I had been permitted to see, almost half a mile below the surface, I knew that I should never again look upon the stars without remembering their active, living counterparts swimming about in that terrific pressure. It leaves the mind in a maze of wonder — to think of having seen these hidden multitudes, many most delicate and fragile, moving swiftly on their missions in life — avoiding their enemies, searching for food and finding mates; and all amid this black, ice-cold water with nearly a half-ton of weight crushing down upon every square inch. The recital of such facts as the pressure of fourteen tons of water on the surface of the window out of which I had been looking, or that the whole bathysphere was resisting a weight of over five thousand tons — these probably mean much to anyone who must think only with his imagination of this strange world. When once it has been seen, it will remain forever the most vivid memory in life, solely because of its cosmic chill and isolation, the eternal and absolute darkness and the indescribable beauty of its inhabitants.

William Beebe (1934) *Half Mile Down*

When William Beebe stood marvelling on the deck of the *Ready*, he had just returned from 2 200 ft down in the ocean, at a time when — as Beebe himself put it — 'only dead men' had been below 300 ft*. It was 22 September 1932, and the *Ready*, a converted barge, was anchored in water about 7 000 ft deep to the south-east of Bermuda. Beebe and his colleague, Otis Barton, had been lowered in a steel 'bathysphere' down through the sunlit surface waters into the dark, where the only lights came from the luminous organs of underwater creatures (Figure 2.1). The bathysphere — a diving bell less than 5 ft in diameter (Figure 2.2) — was connected to the surface by a telephone cable, and for the last 700 ft of the descent Beebe shared his view through the quartz portholes with hundreds of thousands of radio listeners.

In this television age, we are well aware that there are strange and wonderful creatures living in the deep ocean, even if few of us have seen them at first hand. Yet less than 100 years before Beebe's bathysphere went 'half mile down' it was a generally accepted 'truth' that below a certain depth the ocean was totally devoid of life: it was **azoic.** How this belief arose, and why it persisted in the face of evidence to the contrary, is a very interesting — and, for scientists, salutary — story.

2.1 The azoic theory

The origin of the azoic theory can be traced back to the botanist, zoologist and geologist, Edward Forbes (1815–54). While studying bottom-living marine life around the British Isles, Forbes had noticed that within different depth ranges (zones) the sea-bed supports different groups of species, or 'communities' — a situation analogous to the banding or **zonation** of species which can be seen along a rocky shore. In 1842, Forbes undertook a dredging survey of the floor of the Aegean Sea (in an area now known to

---

* We use feet here because this is what Beebe and his US colleagues used: 300 ft is ≈90 m and 2 200 ft is ≈670 m. Later we refer to depths in fathoms, which was the standard unit of depth until relatively recently. 1 fathom = 6 feet = 1.83 m.

Figure 2.1 Illustration from *Half Mile Down,* Beebe's account of the dives made in the bathysphere; the figure is part of a painting by Else Bostelmann. Beebe's original caption read as follows: 'Pale Round-Mouths Pursuing a School of Copepods: The Pale Round-Mouths (*Cyclothone signata*), together with their near relations, are the most abundant of all the deep-sea fish near Bermuda and several hundred are sometimes taken in one net. These are only two inches in length, their tissues soft and flabby, and they are always dead when they reach the surface. I saw them alive a dozen times from the bathysphere, but only when they came very near.'

Figure 2.2 Beebe's bathysphere breaking the surface, before being swung aboard and set down on the deck of the *Ready.* The photograph was taken at the end of the record-breaking dive to 2 200 ft (≈670 m).

be particularly barren), and between the shallows and a depth of 230 fathoms ($\approx$420 m), found eight 'zones' of sea-bed life, analogous to those he had found around Britain. The published summary of his 1844 lecture to the Royal Institution of Great Britain includes the following general conclusion, based on the results of his Aegean survey:

> *The number of [marine] species is much less in the lower zones than in the upper. Vegetables disappear below a certain depth, and the diminution in the number of animals indicates a zero not far distant.*

Forbes continued:

> *The geological application of this fact, of a zero of life in the ocean, is evident. All deposits formed below that zero, will be void, or almost void, of organic contents.*

Forbes was writing about **benthic** (bottom-living) organisms, but he would almost certainly have believed that whatever was true of the deep sea-bed would have been true of the deep water overlying it; in other words, his 'azoic zone' would effectively have encompassed the great bulk of ocean waters, and this is how it was interpreted by others.

Question 2.1 Given what you know about **photosynthesis** explain briefly why 'Vegetables disappear [that is, are no longer found] below a certain depth'. If you can write a simple chemical equation to illustrate your answer, do so. *Hint* Organic matter can be represented in your equation by $C_6H_{12}O_6$, the general formula for carbohydrates.

The azoic theory took root and proved very persistent, despite the fact that there was already quite considerable evidence for the existence of life in the deep ocean. As early as 1818, John Ross's expedition in search of a North-West Passage had inadvertently brought up deep-sea organisms. The expedition was not simply one of exploration; it had been charged with various scientific tasks including investigation of the Earth's magnetic field and the collection of sea-bed samples. It was while bringing up sea-floor mud with a specially designed 'deep-sea clamm' (a kind of metal grab) that Ross's men brought up first a starfish and then a brittlestar, clinging to the line near the 800 fathom marker; furthermore, the mud itself was found to contain worms.

Figure 2.3 James Clark Ross (1800–62) as a young officer. Like his uncle, John Ross, James undertook a considerable amount of oceanographic work during his exploratory expeditions for the British Admiralty.

One of the midshipmen on the *Isabella*, Ross's flagship, was his nephew James Clark Ross (Figure 2.3), who was to become an even greater polar explorer. (James's own flagship, the *Erebus*, would later be equipped with a deep-sea clamm and a dredge, and he also obtained deep-sea creatures from well below 300 fathoms.)

The Rosses were by no means the only investigators to bring organisms up from the so-called 'azoic' zone. For example, in the 1840s, the French scientist Georges Aimé brought up a variety of animals from a depth of 1 800 m off the coast of Algeria, and Henry Goodsir (a member of one of the Arctic expeditions led by Sir John Franklin) brought up a 'capital haul' of animals from a similar depth in the Davis Strait, between Baffin Island and Greenland.

In the nineteenth (and early twentieth) century, depth measurements were made by **sounding** using a weighted line: the weight was lowered until it reached the sea floor (at which time the line went slack) and the length of line let out was assumed to correspond to the depth of the sea-floor.

In the second half of the 1850s, the need to survey submarine routes for telegraph cables (see Chapter 3) led to a sharp increase in the number of deep-sea soundings. For cable-laying it was also necessary to know the nature of the sea-floor, and John Mercer Brooke, a junior officer in the United States Navy, invented a sounding instrument which collected small quantities of sea-floor sediment in a quill (later replaced by a metal tube; see Figure 2.4). Examination of numerous samples of sediment from the deep (>2 000 m) Atlantic sea-floor showed that much of it was covered by calcareous sediment — that is, sediment with a large proportion of calcium carbonate. Particularly noticeable were the remains of foraminiferans (see Figure 2.5b), but there were also other calcareous remains and the remains of diatoms and radiolarians, which are made of hydrated silica (see Box 2.1). Similar results were obtained in the Pacific. Forbes's idea that deep-sea sediments (or 'deposits') were 'void, or almost void, of organic contents' was thus shown to be mistaken, at least as far as some areas of the Atlantic and Pacific were concerned.

Returning to our theme, why *did* the idea of a lifeless abyss persist through much of the nineteenth century? There was almost certainly a mixture of reasons. Perhaps the most important was that — despite occasional indications to the contrary — Forbes's results seemed so conclusive that there was no real incentive to investigate further — particularly as to do so would not be easy. Dredging, or even simply sounding to determine depth, was very difficult and time-consuming in water deeper than a few hundred metres. Furthermore, until the trans-Atlantic telegraph link was thought of, there was no commercial advantage to be gained from investigating the deep sea. No-one fished in deep waters (there seemed little point!) and whales were caught and killed at the surface. Thus, everything of interest or value in the oceans was to be found in shallow or surface waters; the deep sea was something quite different and separate.

But why was evidence of deep-sea life, collected by the Rosses and others, apparently ignored? Or, looked at in a wider context, why was it that *knowledge* of the oceans grew so slowly and inefficiently?

Much of the malaise can be traced back to poor communication, both between the scientists and the surveyors, hydrographers and explorers (who, as we have seen, were responsible for much of the oceanographic work of the time), and among the specialists in the various branches of science (at a time when specialization was becoming intense). This lack of communication was partly due to the fact that although learned societies (The Royal Society, for example) published papers on various aspects of science, there was no publication dealing solely with the science of the sea. Furthermore, although the emerging discipline of geology had been given coherence by Charles Lyell (whose three-volume *Principles of Geology* was first published from 1830 to 1833), there was no similar overall framework for knowledge about the oceans. Thus, advances in the physics, chemistry and biology of the seas remained unrelated to one another, and, being fragmentary, tended to be ignored or forgotten.

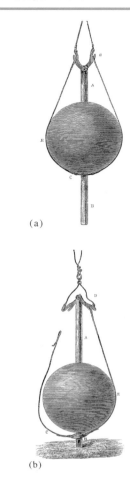

(a)

(b)

Figure 2.4 Brooke's deep-sea sounding apparatus, which also acted as a 'corer'. Numerous modifications were made, but they all depended on a heavy weight being released when the instrument struck the sea-bed. The weight—in this case a 64 lb shot—drove a hollow tube into the sediment; when the instrument was retrieved, the tube contained a sample of sediment, the shot itself remaining behind. The depth to the sea-bed, and the sediment type, could therefore be determined at the same time. Diagram (a) shows the apparatus prior to reaching the sea-bed; (b) shows the release of the weight after it has driven the hollow tube into the sediment. (This illustration is reproduced from *The Depths of the Sea* by Charles Wyville Thomson; see later.)

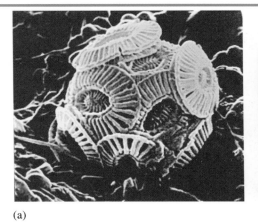

Figure 2.5 (a) A coccolithophore, a single-celled alga, ≈10 μm across, which secretes platelets of calcium carbonate. (b) Tests (that is, shells) of foraminiferans; these are about 50 μm across, but some species are much larger. Coccolithophore platelets (known as 'coccoliths') and the tests of foraminiferans are the principal biogenic components of calcareous oozes.

(a) (b)

Box 2.1 *Sea-floor sediments*

2.1

Much of the deep sea-bed is covered by sediments containing a high proportion of **biogenic** material — that is, material originating from living organisms. When marine plants and animals die and sink down to the sea-floor, their hard parts — shells, tests or skeletons — may survive more-or-less intact. It is accumulations of the hard parts of **phytoplankton** and **zooplankton** — floating microscopic plants and animals (Plate 2.1) — which make up the deep-sea biogenic sediments or **oozes**.

Biogenic sediments may be either predominantly **calcareous** (that is, made of calcium carbonate, $CaCO_3$) or **siliceous** (made of hydrated silica, $SiO_2.H_2O$), or a mixture of the two.

In the deep ocean, calcareous sediments are very often dominated by the remains of coccolithophores (**planktonic** — that is, free-floating — algae) or foraminiferans (small animals, of which there are both planktonic and benthic species); see Figure 2.5.

At high latitudes, deep-sea siliceous sediments are dominated by the remains of diatoms (single-celled planktonic algae); at low latitudes, they are dominated by the skeletons of radiolarians (single-celled planktonic animals); see Figure 2.6.

How much organic material there is in deep-sea sediments depends to a large extent on how productive the overlying surface water is — that is, how much life it supports. The greater the *primary productivity* (rate of growth and reproduction of phytoplankton) the greater the supply of organic material to the sea-bed. However, deep-sea sediments are never 100% biogenic in origin; they also contain varying proportions of clay (commonly referred to as 'pelagic' clay, after the Greek *pelagos* meaning sea). This is formed from the fine-grained products of erosion and weathering on land, which are carried to the ocean partly on the wind but mainly in rivers: being very fine-grained they take a long time to sink and hence may be carried thousands of kilometres from land before reaching the sea-bed. ■

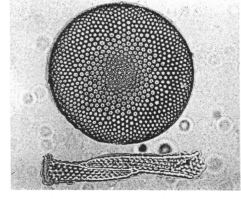

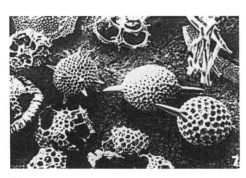

Figure 2.6 (a) Diatoms, the remains of which dominate siliceous sediments at high latitudes; they vary in size from a few μm to around 200 μm. (b) The silica skeletons of radiolarians; radiolarians are single-celled animals and their remains dominate siliceous sediments at low latitudes. They are usually between 50 μm and 300 μm in size.

(a) (b)

Figure 2.7 Charles Wyville Thomson, from an engraving by C. H. Jeens. A Scot, Wyville Thomson first studied in Edinburgh; by the time of his premature death in 1882, he had held professorships in natural history at Cork, Belfast and Edinburgh. His part in our story illustrates the fact that in Britain the development of oceanography was closely linked to an interest in marine biology; this contrasted with the situation in the United States, where the initial impetus to investigate the oceans came from the need for the young country to survey and chart its coasts and inshore waters.

Inextricably linked with the problems outlined above was the lack of any organizational infrastructure for ocean-related science; this in turn resulted from a lack of government funding, on which expensive expeditions depended. This is not to say that valuable work was not undertaken on government-funded voyages of surveying or exploration, of which the most notable were by the French, the Americans and the British.

However, the impetus for exploratory voyages was primarily political, and they were aimed at increasing national wealth and prestige; in the case of the British they were also being used to occupy a large navy, underemployed since the end of the Napoleonic wars. It was therefore perhaps not surprising that the marine scientific work tended to be 'grafted on' and of secondary importance. Very often, the scientific programme was misguided or based on incorrect assumptions, and in some cases put back rather than advanced the growth of understanding of the oceans.

Whatever the reasons, it was to be a long time before schemes for coordinating advances in oceanographic understanding were to become effective, and it is perhaps not surprising that the idea of the deep ocean as a lifeless void persisted, given that the evidence to the contrary was sparse and not widely known. However, this is only part of the story; we can obtain some further insight into why such evidence as there was tended to be ignored or dismissed, by reference to the work of the pioneering marine biologist, Charles Wyville Thomson (1830–82) (Figure 2.7).

2.1.1 The voyages of the Lightning and the Porcupine

Early in his career, Wyville Thomson worked with Forbes, dredging for animals in the Firth of Forth, and for many years he accepted without question Forbes's suggestion of a 'zero of life'. By the mid-1860s, however, he was firmly convinced that the azoic (or 'anti-biotic') theory was untenable; indeed, he had begun to see the deep sea as 'the land of promise for the naturalist'.

In 1867, Wyville Thomson—by now Professor of Natural History at Queen's College, Belfast—visited the eminent Norwegian marine biologist Michael Sars. He was delighted when Sars showed him a collection of animals—many of them new to science—which had been dredged from a depth of 300 fathoms (600 m) off the Lofoten Islands. He saw with excitement that (as he was to write later) 'among them was one of surpassing interest, the small Crinoid … hitherto regarded as extinct'

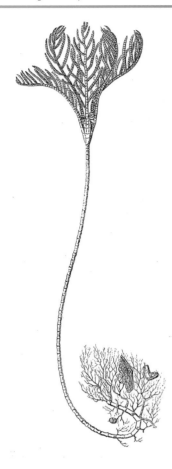

(Figure 2.8). Crinoids—the most primitive living class of echinoderms (the phylum that includes sea-urchins)—were a particular interest of Wyville Thomson's. He and a friend, William Carpenter, had been studying crinoids for some time; they were familiar with the stalkless form ('feather-stars'), but knew the stalked crinoids ('sea-lilies') only from fossils.

Back in Ireland, Wyville Thomson and Carpenter discussed the implications of the Lofoten specimens, and made plans for deep-sea investigations to the west and north of the British Isles. Financial assistance would be essential because both the distance to be travelled before reaching deep water and the labour involved in hauling up deep-sea trawls precluded a privately funded expedition. Carpenter was one of the Vice-Presidents of the Royal Society, so it was agreed that Wyville Thomson should send him a formal letter setting out the academic case for the project. In the letter, Wyville Thomson described what he had seen in Norway and expressed his belief that deep-sea organisms would provide valuable clues as to why and how species evolve (this was only nine years after the publication of Charles Darwin's *Origin of Species*, and debates about evolution were at their height). Wyville Thomson reasoned that it was not surprising that ancient animal forms, or 'living fossils', could be found in the deep sea, given that the 'main cause of the destruction, the migration, and the extreme modification of Animal types, appears to be change of climate', which (he said) only affects the Earth's surface and the upper part of the ocean; he added that 'the temperature of the deep water seems to be constant for all latitudes at 39 [°F or about 4 °C]…'

The Royal Society agreed to cover the cost of equipment, and undertook to request the Admiralty to allow the two scientists to make use of one of the many vessels then stationed on the northern and north-western shores of the British Isles. So it was that in August 1868, Wyville Thomson and Carpenter found themselves sailing north out of Stornaway (in the Western Isles) in HMS *Lightning*—a naval survey ship, barely seaworthy and, according to Wyville Thomson, 'perhaps the very oldest paddle-steamer in her Majesty's navy'. Nevertheless, the voyage was a considerable success from the scientific point of view, and Carpenter was able to write that the dredge hauls proved the existence at depth 'not of a degraded or starved out *residuum* of Animal life, but of a rich and varied Fauna' (see, for example, Figure 2.9).

Figure 2.8   Rhizocrinus loffotensis, the small stalked crinoid or 'sea-lily' (here shown natural size), first found off the Lofoten Islands, and named after them. (From *The Depths of the Sea* by Wyville Thomson.)

Figure 2.9   Two of the many deep-sea animals collected on the first cruise of the *Lightning*, both shown about a third natural size: (a) the starfish *Brisinga*, the first specimens of which had been dredged from 200 fathoms (≈400 m) in a Norwegian fjord (Wyville Thomson placed its nearest relation as the fossil genus *Protaster*); (b) the 'glass sponge', *Holtenia carpentaria*, named after William Carpenter; its body walls consist of a network of spicules made of silica and connected by semi-transparent, elastic tissue. (Both illustrations are from woodcuts in *The Depths of the Sea*.)

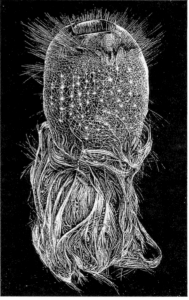

(a)   (b)

Four more deep-water cruises followed, three in 1869 (Figure 2.10a) and one in 1870 (Figure 2.10b). For these, the navy made available HMS *Porcupine*, a small but sturdy survey vessel. The discoveries made during the cruises of the *Lightning* and *Porcupine* were recorded in scientific reports, but it was thought that they should also be made

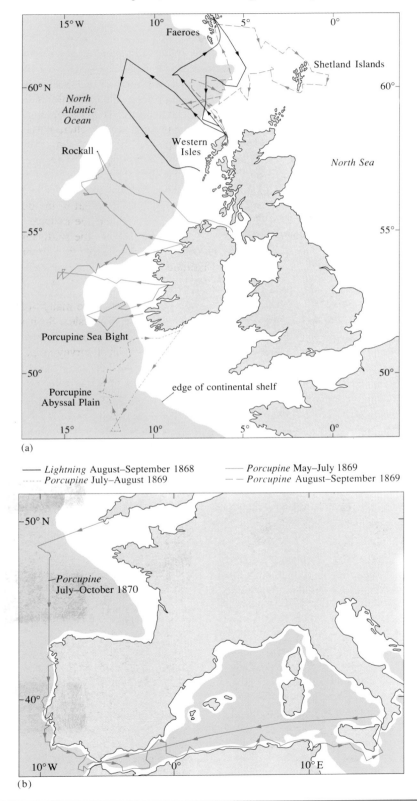

(a)

—— *Lightning* August–September 1868   —— *Porcupine* May–July 1869
‑‑‑‑‑ *Porcupine* July–August 1869   – – *Porcupine* August–September 1869

(b)

Figure 2.10 The tracks of the deep-water cruises of the *Lightning* in 1868 (a) and the *Porcupine* in 1869 and 1870 (a and b). Water deeper than 400 m is shown in blue. (The tracks are taken from charts in *The Depths of the Sea*.)

available to the general public. The account that Wyville Thomson compiled was published in 1873; entitled *The Depths of the Sea*, it was an erudite and comprehensive discussion of discoveries and ideas, and was regarded by many as a literary masterpiece.

2.1.2 Pressure in the ocean

In the first chapter of *The Depths of the Sea*, Wyville Thomson 'set the scientific scene' against which the cruises had been planned. He began by discussing the advances made by Edward Forbes, whom he greatly admired as the first to undertake the systematic study of marine zoology with special reference to the distribution of marine animals in space and time. Then, having outlined the evidence against the azoic theory, he addressed the problem as to why it had survived so long:

> *The enormous pressure at these great depths seemed at first sight alone sufficient to put any idea of life out of the question. There was a curious popular notion, in which I well remember sharing when a boy, that, in going down, the seawater became gradually under the pressure heavier and heavier, and that all the loose things in the sea floated at different levels, according to their specific weight: skeletons of men, anchors and shot and cannon, and last of all the broad gold pieces wrecked in the loss of many a galleon on the Spanish Main; the whole forming a kind of 'false bottom' to the ocean, beneath which there lay all the depth of clear still water, which was heavier than molten gold.*

In succeeding paragraphs, Wyville Thomson went on to show why the pressure at depth in the ocean was not necessarily as inimical to life as might have been thought. In Activity 2.1 you can do the same. First, however, read Box 2.2, to remind yourself about **hydrostatic pressure** in a fluid.

2.2

Box 2.2   Some basic ocean physics

Hydrostatic pressure

Hydrostatic pressure is the pressure at depth in a fluid (that is, a gas or liquid) resulting simply from the weight of overlying fluid. (It is referred to as hydro*static* pressure because no account is taken of the motion of the fluid, which can give rise to a pressure of its own; think of the effect of wind, for example.)

It is easier to think about pressure if we consider the pressure acting on a 'unit area'; in terms of SI units, this means the pressure acting on 1 square metre. So, imagine an area of $1\,m^2$ above which is a column z metres high of a fluid which has a density $\rho\,kg\,m^{-3}$ (Figure 2.11).

We need to calculate the weight of fluid acting on the $1\,m^2$, remembering that weight is given by mass $\times$ g, where g is the acceleration due to gravity (in $m\,s^{-2}$).

▷   Given that the volume of the column is $z\,m \times 1\,m^2 = z\,m^3$, what is the *mass* of fluid in the column? And hence what is the *weight* of fluid in the column?

▶   The mass of fluid is given by volume $\times$ density, and so is $z\,m^3 \times \rho\,kg\,m^{-3} = z\rho\,kg$. To calculate the *weight* of fluid in the column we multiply by g: $(z\rho\,kg) \times (g\,m\,s^{-2}) = z\rho g = \rho g z\,kg\,m\,s^{-2}$.

Notice that the unit of weight is that of mass $\times$ acceleration $\equiv$ force; $1\,kg\,m\,s^{-2}$ is also referred to as 1 newton (1 N). Pressure is given in terms of force (weight) per unit area; our unit area is $1\,m^2$, so the pressure P acting on the bottom of the column is given simply by

$$P = \rho g z\,N\,m^{-2} \qquad (2.1)$$

This is known as the **hydrostatic equation**.

Stability and convection in the ocean

Everybody knows that 'warm air rises'. What we really mean, however, is that 'air that has become *warmer (and hence less dense) than its surroundings* rises'. If we heat a pan of soup over a gas ring, the warmed soup at the bottom expands and so becomes less dense. It

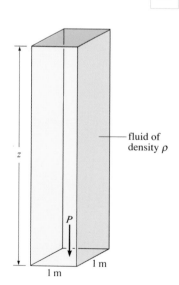

Figure 2.11   A column of fluid z metres high, with a cross-sectional area of $1\,m \times 1\,m = 1\,m^2$. The fluid has a density of $\rho\,kg\,m^{-3}$, and it exerts a pressure P on the bottom of the column.

rises to the top, displacing colder soup, which sinks to the bottom, where it is warmed in turn (Figure 2.12a). This pattern of fluid motion, driven by density differences, is known as **convection**.

There is convection in the ocean too, but with an important difference. In the soup and the atmosphere, convection occurs when the fluid in question is warmed from below; in the case of the ocean, convection occurs when the ocean is *cooled from above*, so that surface waters contract and become denser (Figure 2.12b). The situation in which denser water overlies less dense water is **unstable**, and cannot persist for long. Water denser than that beneath it will sink (not necessarily simply vertically); similarly, water that is less dense than that above it will rise. At any point in the ocean, unless there are unusual circumstances, density will be found to increase with depth; this is the normal **stable** situation. ■

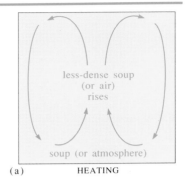

Figure 2.12 Schematic diagrams to illustrate the difference between convection in (a) a pan of soup or the atmosphere, and (b) the ocean. In (a), convection is driven by heating from below; in (b), it is driven by cooling at the surface.

Activity 2.1

This activity helps you to explore the effect of pressure in the deep sea.

(a) (i) Use the hydrostatic equation (Equation 2.1) to calculate the pressure on the sea-bed at a depth of 3 700 m (which we now know to be the average depth of the seas and oceans). The density of seawater is about 1.03×10^3 kg m^{-3}, and $g = 9.8$ m s^{-2}.

(ii) At sea-level, the pressure due to the atmosphere is $\sim 10^5$ N m^{-2}. How many 'atmospheres' are equivalent to 3 700 m of seawater? Or, looked at another way, how many metres of seawater give rise to the same pressure as one atmosphere (also known as one 'bar')?

(b) (i) In the calculations in part (a), what have you been assuming about the degree of compressibility of seawater? If seawater were very compressible, how would this affect the pressure at the deep sea-bed, and why?

(ii) In fact, the assumption referred to in (i) is more or less valid: a parcel of seawater at 10 000 m would occupy a volume only 4% less than it would at the surface, under atmospheric pressure. What bearing does this have on the belief, widespread in Wyville Thomson's youth, that 'in going down, the seawater became under the pressure heavier and heavier…' until eventually 'there lay all the depth of clear still water, which was heavier than molten gold'?

So, though not as great as was once generally believed, the pressure in the deep sea is still considerable; as Wyville Thomson put it, at 2 000 fathoms (≈3 700 m) 'a man would bear upon his body a weight equal to twenty locomotive engines, each with a load of pig iron'. However, unlike some of his contemporaries, he realized that this great pressure would not preclude life in the deep sea, any more than the 'weight' of the atmosphere precludes life on land, because 'an organism supported through all its tissues on all sides, and without, by incompressible fluids at the same pressure, would not necessarily be incommoded by it'.

2.2 The 4-degree fallacy

It wasn't simply the idea of great pressure in the deep sea, or even its perpetual darkness, which caused people to believe that life there was impossible. Rather, it was a mistaken view about the ocean circulation, which stemmed from a fundamental misconception about the physical properties of seawater, namely that they are the same as those of fresh water. In particular, it was the belief that the *density* of seawater varies with *temperature* in the same way as the density of fresh water (Figure 2.13).

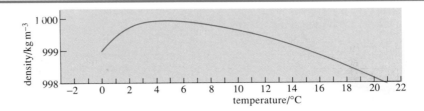

Figure 2.13 The variation with temperature of the density of fresh water.

▷ From Figure 2.13 *describe* how the density of fresh water changes as the temperature decreases.

▶ The density of fresh water increases with decreasing temperature down to about 4 °C (more precisely 3.98 °C; at this temperature the density is nearly 1 000 kg m^{-3}); with further decrease in temperature the density begins to decrease, so that by freezing point (0 °C) it is about 999 kg m^{-3}.

In other words, fresh water has its maximum density at a temperature of about 4 °C.

One of those who believed that this was also true of seawater was the polar explorer, James Clark Ross (Figure 2.3). During his three-year exploration of Antarctic waters (1839–43), Ross conscientiously observed the temperature of the sea, taking measurements as deep as 1 200 fathoms (≈2 200 m). On the basis of these observations he decided that there must be a 'circle of mean temperature' around the globe at latitude 56° S (Figure 2.14), where he believed that[*]:

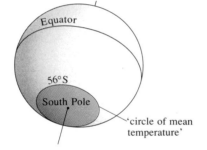

Figure 2.14 Ross's 'circle of mean temperature'.

> *the mean temperature of the sea obtains throughout its entire depth ... To the north of this circle the sea has become warmer than its mean temperature, by reason of the Sun's heat, which it has absorbed, elevating its temperature at various depths in different latitudes. So that the line of mean temperature of 39.5° [≈4 °C], in latitude 45° S, has descended to the depth of 600 fathoms; and at the equatorial and tropical regions, this mark of the limit of the Sun's influence is found at the depth of about 1,200 fathoms; beneath which the ocean maintains its unvarying mean temperature of 39.5°, whilst that of the surface is about 78°.*
>
> *So likewise to the south of the circle of mean temperature ... near the 70th degree of latitude, we find the line of mean temperature has descended to the depth of 750 fathoms; beneath which again, to the greatest depths, the temperature of 39.5° obtains, whilst that of the surface is 30°.*

Figure 2.15 shows what Ross imagined a north–south temperature section of the ocean would look like. Ross was referring specifically to southern latitudes but something similar (though not necessarily identical) was thought to obtain in northern latitudes.

Activity 2.2

By reference to the above quotation and to Figure 2.13, try to suggest in about 150 words how Ross thought the situation shown in Figure 2.15 would come about. (Ross didn't subscribe to the idea that compression would cause deep ocean waters to become 'heavier than molten gold'.)

[*] This quotation is taken from Sir James Clark Ross's book *A Voyage of Discovery and Research in the Southern and Antarctic Regions, during the Years 1839–1843*, published in two volumes in 1847.

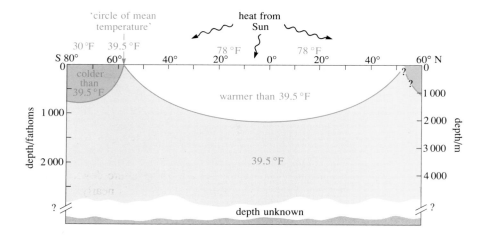

Figure 2.15 Schematic north–south cross-section through the Atlantic Ocean (ignoring the curvature of the Earth), between 80° S and 60° N, to show how Ross imagined temperature to vary with depth and latitude. He thought that there were three main regions: water that was warmer than 39.5 °F 'by reason of the Sun's heat' (untoned), water at 39.5 °F (mid-blue tone) and water colder than 39.5 °F (dark blue tone).

Figure 2.16 shows how the density of 'average' seawater actually varies with temperature, and Figure 2.17 shows, in broad terms, what we now know about the vertical temperature distribution of the Atlantic Ocean. Also shown is the large-scale pattern of meridional (north–south) current flow, below the wind-driven surface layer.

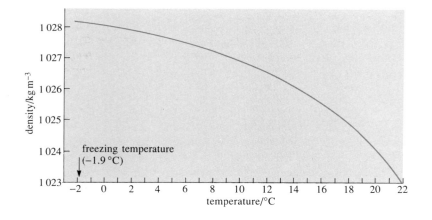

Figure 2.16 The variation with temperature of the density of average seawater, which has a concentration of dissolved ions of about 35 g l⁻¹.

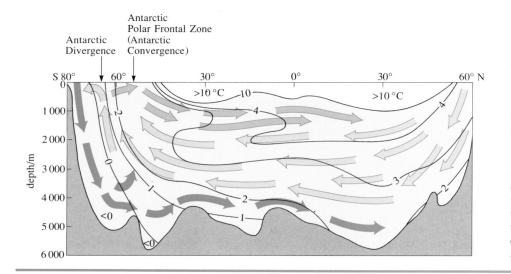

Figure 2.17 Generalized north–south temperature cross-section of the Atlantic Ocean between 80° S and 60° N; the lines of equal temperature (°C) are known as **isotherms**. Also shown are the main features of the deep circulation. At the Antarctic Polar Frontal Zone (or Antarctic Convergence), Antarctic surface waters flowing north converge with warmer sub-tropical waters and sink beneath them; at the Antarctic Divergence, water that sank in high northern latitudes eventually reaches the surface again.

Activity 2.3   You should spend up to 15 minutes on this activity.

(a) (i)   Figure 2.17 illustrates how water sinks at high latitudes and flows down into the deep ocean (cf. Figure 2.12). What determines the depth to which it sinks?

(ii) By reference to Figure 2.17, identify the coldest water in the ocean. From Figure 2.16, what can you say about the lowest temperature to be found in the oceans?

(iii) Given that seawater can only be cooled while in contact with the atmosphere, what is the significance of the fact that ice is less dense than water?

(b) By reference to Figure 2.17, try to suggest other factors, not appreciated by Ross and his contemporaries, which also affect the pattern of circulation in the oceans.

So the circulatory pattern within the body of the ocean is determined by processes occurring at the surface: at **divergences**, surface waters driven apart by winds are replaced by water welling up from below; at **convergences**, surface waters come together under the influence of wind and may sink. Furthermore, the temperature of a parcel of water within the body of the ocean will have been determined while it was at the surface.

Another important characteristic of ocean water which is determined while it is at the surface is the extent to which it has dissolved within it atmospheric gases such as oxygen.

▷   Given that marine organisms need to **respire** — to oxidize organic substances, and thereby release energy — now see if you can suggest why the scenario shown in Figure 2.15 might lead people to think that there was no life in the deep ocean or on the deep sea-bed.

▶   Once water at 4 °C sank (initially to the bottom, but later to overlie 'older' water), it would remain there for ever, stagnant. Water sinking down from the surface would carry with it oxygen dissolved from the atmosphere, which marine organisms could use in respiration; however, once this oxygen was used up, it could not be replenished because no 'new' oxygen-rich water could flow down through the existing 'reservoir' of 4 °C water (to do that it would have to be denser). According to the scenario shown in Figure 2.15, therefore, the deep sea was not only dark, cold, at high pressure and stagnant, but also anoxic (without oxygen), and so would therefore be very unlikely to support life.

In reality, cold ocean water which has sunk down into the deep oceans from the surface at high latitudes is particularly well oxygenated because cold water can contain more dissolved oxygen than can warm water. Nevertheless, it is perhaps understandable that the azoic theory was accepted without question, given the belief in the 4 °C maximum density of seawater. But, as Wyville Thomson commented, 'It is singular that this belief should have met with so general acceptance, for so early as the year 1833 M. Depretz determined that the temperature of the maximum density of seawater, which contracts steadily till just above its freezing-point, is −3°67 C[*]; and even before that time observations of sea-temperatures at great depths, which were certainly trustworthy within a few degrees, had indicated several degrees below the freezing-point of fresh water.'

In fact, Wyville Thomson was mistaken in thinking that Depretz had been the first to determine a value for the temperature of maximum density of seawater in the labora-

---

[*] This means −3.67 °C, but don't worry about the precise value. The important point is that the value is well below 4 °C, and close to the freezing temperature estimated by Depretz.

tory. This honour belongs to Alexander Marcet, a Swiss living in London, who, with his friend Smithson Tennant, developed techniques for analysing natural waters. In 1807, Tennant was given a sample of water from the Dead Sea. The two were discussing its analysis when, according to Marcet, 'it occurred to us that a chemical examination of different seas, in a variety of latitudes and at different depths, might be interesting; and that, however unlikely to be productive of any striking discovery, such an enquiry, conducted with due care and attention might afford curious results, and throw some light on this obscure subject'.

Eventually, Marcet was to have obtained nearly 70 samples collected from all over the world, but he published a report in 1819, based on analysis of sixteen of them. The report was entitled 'On the specific gravity, and temperature of sea waters, in different parts of the ocean, and in particular seas; with some account of their saline contents'. It contained a number of important conclusions, not the least of which was that concerning the variation of the density of seawater with temperature: Marcet demonstrated clearly that in contrast to the density of fresh water (Figure 2.13), the density of seawater increases down to its freezing temperature (which he put at 22 °F ($\approx$−5.6 °C), rather than −1.9 °C; see Figure 2.16).

Marcet also made an important discovery about the chemistry of seawater: he found that all the samples of seawater 'however different their strength, contained the same ingredients all over the world, these bearing very nearly the same proportions to each other...'. In other words, whatever the total concentration of dissolved ions (that is, the **salinity** of the water—see Box 2.3), the proportions of the various ions one to another remain the same. Today, this is referred to by oceanographers as the **constancy of composition** of seawater.

You will meet salinity again in Chapter 4, so it is worth saying a little more about it here.

Box 2.3   The salinity of seawater

Seawater tastes salty because it contains a high concentration of dissolved **ions** (loosely referred to as 'dissolved salts'), mostly derived from the weathering of rocks and carried to the sea in rivers.

The concentration of dissolved ions in seawater — its salinity — may be between about 32 and 37 parts per thousand (‰) by mass, that is, between about 32 and 37 grams of dissolved ions per kilogram of seawater; 'average' seawater has a salinity of 35 g kg^{-1} or approximately 35 g l^{-1}. Today, the salinity of seawater is determined from its electrical conductivity and, for reasons that we do not need to go into here, is written without a unit. The symbol used for salinity is S; so, for 'average' seawater, $S = 35$ (or 35‰).

Nearly all of the 88 naturally occurring elements have been measured or detected in seawater, mostly in dissolved form. However, 99.9% of the dissolved material in seawater is made up of only eleven ions. They are (in order of decreasing abundance): Cl$^-$, Na$^+$, SO$_4^{2-}$, Mg^{2+}, Ca^{2+}, K$^+$, HCO$_3^-$, Br$^-$, H$_2$BO$_3^-$, Sr^{2+} and F$^-$ (you do not need to remember this list). ∎

▷   While working through Activity 2.3, you may have noticed that the water sinking from the Antarctic Polar Frontal Zone and flowing northwards towards the Equator (mid-blue arrows in Figure 2.17) flows *above* water that is slightly *warmer* (pale-blue arrows). At first sight, this may seem to be an impossible situation, given that density increases with depth at every point in the ocean. How would you explain this apparent paradox, in the light of what you have just been reading?

▶   The density of seawater is determined not only by its temperature (and to a small extent pressure), but also by its salinity. It is therefore possible for warm water to be denser than cold water by virtue of its higher salinity.

The body of water (or 'water mass') represented by the mid-blue arrows forms in a region of high precipitation and summer ice-melt. It therefore has a lower salinity ($\approx$34.2) than the body of water represented by the light-blue arrows (which has undergone high net evaporation and has a salinity close to 35). These two water masses are known as Antarctic Intermediate Water and North Atlantic Deep Water, respectively. As mentioned in the answer to Activity 2.3, part (a) (ii), the very cold and dense water mass (dark blue arrows) that flows northwards beneath North Atlantic Deep Water is known as Antarctic Bottom Water.

Because the deep circulation of the ocean is determined by both temperature and salinity, it is also known as the **thermohaline circulation.**

2.2.1 Deep-sea temperature measurements

Returning to our theme of the 4 °C fallacy, you may have been wondering why it was that deep-sea temperature measurements seemed to *support* the idea, rather than disprove it. In fact, deep water had been shown to be colder than 4 °C on a number of occasions. For example, in 1818, John Ross's Arctic expedition had made temperature readings at fixed locations, and found that temperature decreased with depth to well below 0 °C; moreover, mud brought up from the bottom by the deep-ocean clamm was also found to be below 0 °C. However, the majority of deep-sea temperature readings gave values greater than $\approx$4.4 °C and it was supposed that Ross's readings were erroneous. Furthermore, Marcet had died in 1822, and could not defend his experimental technique against those who said that in determining the density–temperature relationship of seawater he had not allowed for the effect of cold on his equipment.

So, given that the bulk of deep-ocean water has temperatures below 4 °C (Figure 2.17), why were such temperatures not generally recorded? The answer lies in the instrumentation used. For much of the nineteenth century, the thermometers used for deep-sea work were based on the maximum and minimum thermometer designed by James Six around 1780 (Figure 2.18). Originally devised for meteorological use, it worked on the same principle as the maximum and minimum thermometers used today in greenhouses (for more details, see caption). Because of the difficulties of lowering such a delicate instrument over the side of a vessel when it was rolling and pitching in the open ocean, the thermometer was usually protected by a case, perforated at top and bottom to allow a through-flow of water.

> ▷ Given the instrumentation available, try to suggest why measurements of deep-sea temperatures tended to be erroneously high.

> ▶ The pressure at depth would compress the glass tubing, especially the central bulb. The alcohol would be 'squeezed' down the right-hand tube, pushing the mercury down and around the bend, to some extent offsetting the effect of contraction, and causing the 'minimum' marker to read high. (Curiously, it ought to have been obvious that this would happen, since the alcohol and mercury could be moved simply by the pressure of finger and thumb on the bulb.)

Over the years, Six's thermometer went through various modifications and improvements, and was brought as close to perfection as was possible in the version now known as the Miller–Casella thermometer (after its designer and manufacturer, respectively). The Miller–Casella thermometer was both compact and sensitive (by virtue of having a very fine bore); more importantly, it was protected against pressure. The bulb and tube were surrounded by an outer glass shell and the space between filled with alcohol vapour that had been warmed to expel most of the air before the

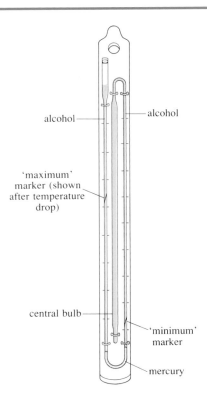

Figure 2.18 Six's original 'self-registering' thermometer. The bend of the U-tube was occupied by mercury; alcohol completely filled the central bulb and the right-hand limb of the tube above the mercury, and partly filled the left-hand limb. Warming would cause the alcohol in the central bulb plus the right-hand limb to expand, driving the mercury around the bend, so that it pushed a light steel marker sealed in glass up the left-hand tube. When the temperature fell, and the mercury retreated back down, the marker was prevented from falling by a springy glass 'tail' and its position thus recorded the maximum temperature attained; meanwhile, a similar marker in the right-hand tube would be pushed upwards by the mercury, and would then stick at a position corresponding to the lowest temperature reached. After use, the thermometer was re-set by positioning the markers at the top of the mercury columns, using a magnet. (The thermometer readings were determined solely by the expansion and contraction of the alcohol in the bulb and right-hand limb; the effect of temperature change on the mercury and the alcohol in the left-hand limb was ignored.)

shell was sealed; thus distortion due to pressure could be taken up by the outer shell, while the alcohol vapour acted as a heat conductor. The Miller–Casella 'protected' thermometer was produced in 1869, and Wyville Thomson wrote of it as follows: 'We depended upon this thermometer in our subsequent cruises in the 'Porcupine', and we found it most satisfactory'; by contrast, when unprotected thermometers had been used on the *Lightning* the previous year, 'Many of the instruments were very wild at a few hundred fathoms, and several gave way under the pressure.' According to Wyville Thomson, John Ross had used some kind of protected thermometer during his 1818 expedition; this explains why he managed to obtain deep-sea temperature readings below 4 °C.

But the existence of 'protected' deep-sea thermometers did not in the least guarantee their being used. One of the reasons for the continued survival of the 4 °C myth was its enthusiastic support by the French explorer Jules-Sébastien-César Dumont d'Urville (Figure 2.19), as a result of temperature measurements made during the exploratory voyage of the *Astrolabe* in 1837–40. As leader of the expedition, Dumont d'Urville had gone to the eminent scientist François Arago, for advice on how best to go about measuring deep-sea temperatures. Arago provided him with unprotected maximum and minimum thermometers; for use on the voyage, they were encased in metal cylinders, but these were not watertight. On one occasion, a thermometer was retrieved from a depth of 1 160 fathoms ($\approx$2 120 m); when someone accidentally touched the bulb it exploded, and Dumont d'Urville realized that it had been weakened by pressure and that his temperature readings could be unreliable.

As no scientist seemed interested in writing up the temperature results, Dumont d'Urville eventually reported them himself. Furthermore, he put them together with all the important deep-ocean temperature measurements that he could track down, arranging the data by depth and longitude. Mysteriously, he ignored the effect of pressure on deep-water data and, as a result, the picture he formed of the distribution of temperature in the ocean resembled that being formulated (at about the same time) by James

Figure 2.19 Jules-Sébastien-César Dumont d'Urville (1790–1842).

Clark Ross (Figure 2.15): below a certain depth, which varied with latitude, the whole of the ocean was filled with water at about 4.4 °C.

Neither Dumont d'Urville nor Ross was a scientist, and, as far as the temperature measurements were concerned, both had been badly advised by those who were.

▷   To what extent would you say Dumont d'Urville and Ross *were* at fault?

▶   Both had direct experience of the effect of pressure on thermometers at depth; pressure sufficient to destroy thermometers might be expected to affect the readings, given that they could be affected by merely pressing the bulb. Ross, furthermore, while working with his uncle John Ross—who used thermometers protected against pressure—had actually *seen* temperature readings of considerably less than 4 °C.

It is probably fair to say that, in the face of an established and seductive theory, Ross and Dumont d'Urville ignored evidence and personal experience. In other words, they interpreted the data as fitting the theory, when closer inspection would have showed that there were disparities.

Despite using pressure-sensitive thermometers, both Ross and Dumont d'Urville managed to detect real oceanographic features. For example, Dumont d'Urville found that the boundary between warm 'surface' water and cold 'deep' water is much shallower in the vicinity of the Equator than in mid-latitudes; as mentioned in the answer to Activity 2.3, Ross's circle of mean temperature near 60° S corresponds to the Antarctic Polar Frontal Zone (or Antarctic Convergence), where cold Antarctic water sinks below warm sub-tropical water. Both of these features can be seen in Figure 2.17.

2.3 The launch of the Challenger Expedition

The deep-water voyages of the *Lightning* and the *Porcupine* between 1868 and 1870 put Britain in the forefront of marine science. By 1871, however, other nations were becoming active: the United States was planning a cruise in the Atlantic and Pacific Oceans, Germany was planning an Atlantic expedition and Sweden had sent two ships to the Arctic. The scientific journal *Nature* commented that if an opportunity were not soon provided for following up earlier work the initiative would be lost, and this would be unfair to those scientists whose efforts had put Britain in her current superior position.

In a lecture at the Royal Institution, Carpenter called on the government not to let Britain's lead in marine science go by default. He felt that the techniques developed on the Atlantic cruises of the *Lightning* and the *Porcupine* should be put to use in the other oceans of the world, and he therefore set about mobilizing the Royal Society and the British Association to promote the idea of a government-sponsored scientific circumnavigation of the globe. Carpenter also used his influence with the Prime Minister, Gladstone, whom he knew socially, to try to ensure that the plan would be accepted as quickly as possible. The government was sympathetic: if a naval vessel were used, the cost would not be significantly higher than that of merely keeping it in commission and paying the officers and ratings. Another important factor was that the expedition was intended to consolidate work already begun, and so any funds allocated to it could be seen as a 'one off'; this made it a much more attractive proposition than the beginning of an ongoing programme of work which would be a continuing drain on government funds.

Figure 2.20 The steam-assisted corvette HMS *Challenger*.

The vessel chosen was the steam-assisted corvette HMS *Challenger* (Figure 2.20). The Royal Society was given the task of appointing the scientists; as Carpenter himself did not want to go to sea again, the obvious choice to lead the team was his friend and colleague, Wyville Thomson. Also appointed were a chemist, John Buchanan (Figure 2.21a; he will appear in our story later) and three naturalists, of whom one — John Murray (Figure 2.21b) — was to become a driving force in oceanography.

(a)

(b)

Figure 2.21 (a) John Buchanan (1844–1925), chemist on the *Challenger* Expedition; (b) John Murray (1841–1914), who took over the herculean task of editing the Expedition Report, after Wyville Thomson died, exhausted, in 1882.

Thus, by December 1872, Carpenter's idea had become a reality. HMS *Challenger*— guns removed and laboratories installed—set out from Portsmouth on the expedition that is now thought of as marking the birth of modern oceanography.

Summary of Chapter 2

1   Until the 1860s, almost all scientists and seamen were firmly convinced that, below the surface layers, the ocean and underlying sea-bed were azoic, that is, life-less. This belief persisted partly because of the status of Edward Forbes, whose 'azoic theory' seemed well founded, partly because the incidences of animals being brought out of deep water were not widely known, and partly because of misunderstandings about the nature of seawater (see points 2 and 4).

2   Fresh water has a density maximum at a temperature of $\approx 4\,°C$. The assumption that seawater *also* has its maximum density at this temperature led people to believe that the deep ocean was filled with a stagnant, anoxic 'reservoir' of $4\,°C$ water. This belief was confirmed rather than refuted by deep-sea temperature measurements, which until the late 1860s were mostly obtained using thermometers that had not been protected against the effect of pressure; consequently the readings were too high. Alexander Marcet was probably the first to demonstrate that seawater behaves differ-ently: its density increases right down to its freezing temperature of $-1.9\,°C$.

3   Seawater is saline because of its high concentration of dissolved ions, notably Cl^-, Na^+, SO_4^{2-}, Mg^{2+}, Ca^{2+}, K^+ and HCO_3^-. The salinity of 'average' seawater is $35\,g\,l^{-1}$ (written as 35). Marcet discovered that whatever the salinity of a sample of seawater, and regardless of where in the ocean it comes from, the relative proportions of the various ions remain the same; this is known as the constancy of composition of seawater.

4   Seawater is only very slightly compressible; the density of deep water and hence the pressure at depth are therefore not as great as was once commonly imagined. Hydrostatic pressure P at a depth z in the ocean is given by the hydrostatic equation, $P = \rho g z$, where ρ is the density (strictly, average density) of overlying seawater and g is the acceleration due to gravity. $10\,m$ of water exerts a pressure equal to 1 bar ($10^5\,N\,m^{-2}$); hence $1\,m$ water $\equiv 1$ decibar.

5   Contrary to what Forbes believed, deep-sea sediments may have a significant pro-portion of biogenic material. Such sediments (oozes) may be siliceous, calcareous or a mixture of the two: siliceous sediments contain the remains of diatoms (plants) or radiolarians (animals); calcareous sediments are usually dominated by the remains of coccolithophores (plants) or foraminiferans (animals). All deep-sea sediments have a proportion of fine-grained pelagic clay.

6   The deep circulation of the ocean is driven by density differences (that is, it is a type of convection); as the density of seawater is determined by its temperature and salinity (plus pressure), the term thermohaline circulation is also used. Water sinks in regions where the wind pattern causes surface waters to come together (convergences) and rises to the surface in regions where winds cause surface waters to move apart (divergences).

7   The deep-sea voyages of the *Lightning* (1868) and the *Porcupine* (1869 and 1870) were the forerunners of the much better known *Challenger* Expedition (1872–4), now thought of as marking the birth of modern oceanography. The impetus for the *Light-ning* and the *Porcupine* voyages came from Charles Wyville Thomson, who believed that the 'azoic theory' was untenable and that, furthermore, the deep sea might contain 'living fossils' which would throw some light on the mechanisms of evolution. It was because of this possibility that the Royal Society was persuaded to help fund the Expedition and to request the assistance of the Admiralty.

8 Factors that can determine whether particular scientific investigations are undertaken include the following: preconceived ideas (the deep sea was ignored for so long because it was believed to be lifeless—see points 1 and 2); commercial factors (the numbers of deep-sea soundings increased sharply with the advent of submarine telegraph cables); and political expediency (as in the case of exploratory voyages). You will come across further examples of the influence of politics later, particularly in Chapter 4.)

Question 2.2 As mentioned in Section 2.1, exploratory voyages such as those led by the Rosses or Dumont d'Urville were primarily aimed at increasing national prestige, and as a result, scientific work tended to be 'grafted on' and of secondary importance. Suggest a modern parallel to this situation.

Question 2.3 On the basis of your answer to Activity 2.1a, and assuming that seawater is completely incompressible, show on Figure 2.22 how hydrostatic pressure varies with depth in the ocean (ignore variations of temperature and salinity with depth). How would your graph look different if you had included the effect of compressibility?

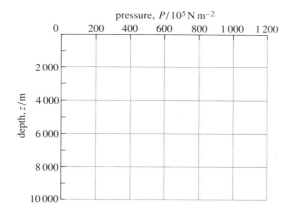

Figure 2.22 Axes for graph of pressure against depth in the ocean (for use with Question 2.3).

Question 2.4 Even when protected against pressure, maximum and minimum thermometers (Figure 2.18) had an inherent disadvantage as far as studying the temperature of the ocean was concerned. To see what this was, imagine that such a thermometer is lowered to a depth of $2\,000\,\text{m}$ at $15°\,\text{S}$ (Figure 2.17); explain why, when retrieved, it has not recorded the temperature at $2\,000\,\text{m}$. Why would this disadvantage not have occurred to Ross and his contemporaries?

3 From lifeless abyss to cradle of creation

In 1853, Cyrus Field, founder of the Atlantic Telegraph Company, was considering how best to lay cable between Newfoundland and Ireland. He wrote to a fellow American, Matthew Fontaine Maury, for advice on the nature of the sea-bed along the proposed route. Maury, a naval officer and hydrographer, was at the time working on the first ever contour map of the Atlantic basin (Figure 3.1). The map was based on some 200 deep soundings; Maury rightly distrusted some of the depths recorded, but soundings made in mid-ocean from the well-equipped vessel *Dolphin* were more reliable and had revealed a wide topographic high in the ocean floor. Maury first named this feature Dolphin Rise, then Middle Ground. Middle Ground (which is not labelled as such on Figure 3.1) is shown as extending down from the northern limit of the map to about 20° N.

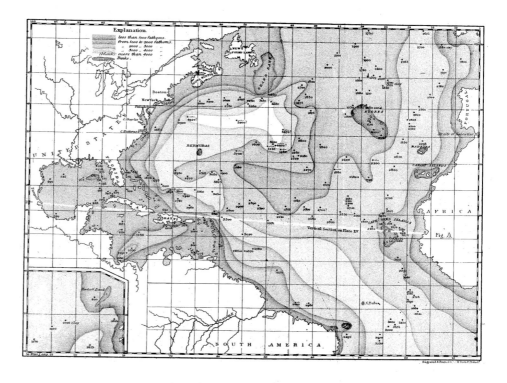

Figure 3.1 Maury's bathymetric* contour map of the North Atlantic; the depths are given in fathoms. (This version appeared in the second edition of Maury's *Physical Geography of the Sea*, published in 1857 by Sampson Low and Son.)

▷ What do we know Middle Ground as today? On the basis of present knowledge, how would you describe its topography? What are the broad deep regions to either side of it?

---

* Present-day bathymetric maps (maps showing the shape of the sea-floor, often in terms of depths below sea-level) are generally made by contouring, using depths obtained by echo-sounding. First developed to detect icebergs in the wake of the *Titanic* disaster, echo-sounding technology was improved during the First World War for the detection of German U-boats; it was further refined during the Second World War for use in mine-hunting instruments, from which developed side-scan sonar systems like *GLORIA* (mentioned in Section 4.1).

► It is part of the Mid-Atlantic Ridge, the spreading axis at which new Atlantic sea-floor forms. Its volcanic topography is very rough, although the further the sea-floor has moved away from the ridge, cooling, contracting and subsiding as it goes, the more it becomes overlain by sediments—clay and organic detritus (Box 2.1) which rain down from above. Eventually, the rough topography is completely covered by sediment: the deep, flat regions that result are known as **abyssal plains** (Figure 3.2).

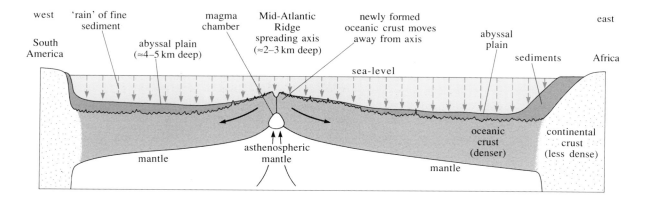

The telegraph cable would clearly have to traverse Middle Ground but, on the basis of 30 soundings along the 3 000-km route, Maury felt able to reply encouragingly to Field, saying that 'the bottom of the sea between the two places [Newfoundland and Ireland] is a plateau which seems to have been placed there for the purpose of holding the wires of a submarine telegraph...'. He later compounded his error by naming the area 'Telegraphic Plateau'.

The first trans-Atlantic cable was laid in 1858, but it failed within three months, and it was not until 1866 that the two sides of the Atlantic were finally linked. Thereafter, various commercial companies laid great lengths of cable over the sea-bed and, as each project involved a sounding survey, much was learnt about the bottom topography, at least along certain routes. The design of sounding machines continued to improve (cf. Figure 2.4), and vessels surveying the cable routes collected not simply broken lengths of older cable (sometimes encrusted with animals, cf. Section 2.1) but also samples of sea-floor sediments.

3.1 The continuity of the chalk

In 1857, the eminent natural scientist Thomas Henry Huxley was asked to examine some sediment samples brought up from the Telegraphic Plateau by Royal Navy cable surveyors in HMS *Cyclops*. Examining the sediment under the microscope, Huxley saw that much of it consisted of the calcareous remains of minute planktonic plants (Figure 3.3), and he was struck by its similarity to the material making up the chalk hills and cliffs of southern England. Indeed, by pulverizing a piece of chalk and shaking it up with water, he could produce something so like the ooze that his colleagues could not distinguish between the two. Huxley deduced that the chalk formations had originated in the deep sea as oozes and over the course of geological time had been compacted and uplifted to their present positions.

We now know that, even though chalk deposits *may* form in the deep ocean, the chalk hills of southern England are made up of coccolithophores (and other organisms) that lived in the *shallow seas* that once covered much of the European continental mass.

Figure 3.2 Schematic cross-section of the Atlantic Ocean (not to scale). Hot, buoyant **asthenosphere** rises at the Mid-Atlantic Ridge **spreading axis** (or **constructive plate margin**) and releases partial melts to form magma. These magmas either solidify at depth within the crust or are erupted on to the sea-bed as lavas. As this newly formed oceanic crust moves away from the spreading axis, it cools, becoming denser, and therefore contracts and subsides. The rough volcanic topography of newly formed ocean floor becomes progressively buried by a 'rain' of silts, clays and organic detritus, with the result that the abyssal plains (which lie about 2 km deeper than the ridge axis) are the flattest regions on Earth, and are underlain by 1–2 km of sediments.

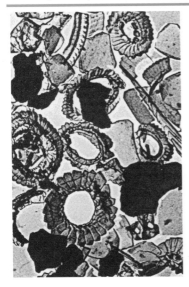

Figure 3.3 The calcareous platelets (or, as Huxley named them, 'coccoliths') of the species of coccolithophore shown in Figure 2.5a. The platelets are a few micrometres across. This species was to be named *Coccolithus huxleyi* after Huxley (it is also sometimes called *Emiliania huxleyi*).

▷ In the light of what you know about oceanic crust (Figure 3.2), why would chalk formed in the deep ocean be unlikely to be transformed into chalk formations on land?

▶ As shown in Figure 3.2, oceanic crust is denser than continental crust and 'floats' on the mantle at a lower level. Chalk formed on oceanic crust would be unlikely to find its way up onto continental crust. (In very unusual circumstances, oceanic crust with its covering of sediments *can* be pushed up onto land, forming **ophiolite sequences**.)

Interestingly, the last chapter of Wyville Thomson's *Depths of the Sea*, written a decade later, is entitled 'The Continuity of the Chalk'. In it Wyville Thomson came to the same conclusion as Huxley: 'There can be no doubt whatever that we have forming at the bottom of the present ocean, a vast sheet of rock which very closely resembles chalk; and there can be little doubt that the old chalk … was produced in the same manner, and under closely similar circumstances; and not the chalk only but most probably all the great limestone formations.'

3.2 The strange story of Bathybius

In 1868, Huxley had occasion to re-examine samples of sea-floor mud collected by the *Cyclops* in 1857. To his surprise, he saw that the surface of the ooze was covered by a thin layer of mucus-like jelly, in which were entangled clusters of tiny granules. Examining the jelly under the microscope he saw that the granules tended to shift slowly about, and he came to the conclusion that 'the granule heaps and the transparent gelatinous matter in which they are imbedded represent masses of protoplasm' ('protoplasm' was the name of the organic substance believed to be the basis of all life). He believed he had discovered a large single-celled organism, and named it *Bathybius haeckelii*, in honour of the German naturalist Ernst Haeckel. Haeckel was one of the foremost exponents of the theory of 'abiogenesis', and when he examined a sample of *Bathybius* he saw it as the spontaneously generating 'primordial slime' ('Urschleim' in German), from which all other living things had developed (Figure 3.4). Thus, in one step, the deep sea had been transformed from a lifeless abyss into the very cradle of life.

Over the next few years several other naturalists reported that they, too, had found *Bathybius* in samples of sea-floor sediment. It had been hopes of finding primitive life forms (and of testing Huxley's theory of 'the continuity of the chalk') which had provided such a powerful incentive for the first deep-sea expeditions—those of the *Lightning* and the *Porcupine*, discussed in Section 2.1. As we have seen, these expeditions provided plenty of evidence for the existence of life in the deep sea, but they did little to solve the mystery of the beginning of life and its subsequent evolution. Nevertheless, Wyville Thomson (who continued to believe strongly in the existence of 'living fossils') wrote in his *Depths of the Sea* that '[now] every haul of the dredge seems to bring to light new and unfamiliar forms—forms which link themselves strangely with the inhabitants of past periods in the earth's history'.

Wyville Thomson hoped to find living fossils during the *Challenger* Expedition, but as one of the naturalists, Henry Nottidge Moseley, put it, 'Such hopes were doomed to disappointment'. He went on '…even to the very last, every cuttlefish that came up in our deep-sea net was squeezed to see if it had a Belemnite's bone in its back and Trilobites were eagerly looked for … Large numbers of interesting animals were obtained … but we picked up no missing links to fill up the gaps in the great zoological family tree'.

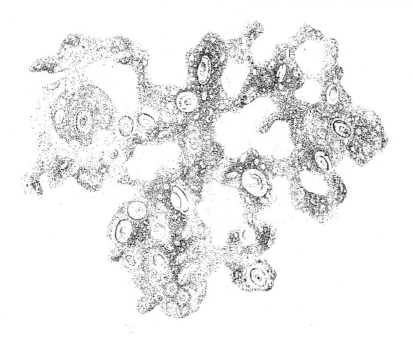

Figure 3.4 A woodcut showing a sample of *Bathybius*, from a publication by Dr Ernst Haeckel. This was reproduced in *The Depths of the Sea*, in which Wyville Thomson describes a sample of *Bathybius* dredged from the Bay of Biscay during the 1870 cruise of the *Porcupine*.

The other hope, of course, was to bring up samples of deep-sea mud with its covering of *Bathybius* in place, but here again the scientists were disappointed. Then, two years after the *Challenger* had set out from Portsmouth and was en *route* for Japan, it was noticed that the sediment samples which had been collected early in the voyage and were preserved in alcohol did indeed have a gelatinous covering, although those samples kept in seawater had none. The Expedition's chemist, John Buchanan (Figure 2.21a), tested the jelly and found that it was nothing more than hydrated calcium sulphate ($CaSO_4.2H_2O$), which had formed as a result of the addition of the alcohol to the wet mud. Buchanan wrote home to his friend and former professor, Alexander Crum Brown, telling him of his discovery, and Brown subsequently entertained his friends by showing them how to make *Bathybius* for themselves!

You too could make *Bathybius*.

▷ How do you think the calcium sulphate formed? In other words, where did the calcium ions and sulphate ions come from?

▶ The calcium ions (Ca^{2+}) and the sulphate ions (SO_4^{2-}) can only have come from seawater (see Section 2.2). The resulting calcium sulphate was dispersed within the alcohol to form a gel.

Learning of Buchanan's experiments, Huxley wrote an open letter to the scientific journal *Nature*, freely admitting that he had made a mistake. Nevertheless, many scientists were unwilling to believe that he could have been wrong. As much as three years after the return of the *Challenger* Expedition, the President of the British Association used his presidential address to support the existence of *Bathybius*; this put Huxley, who was seconding the vote of thanks, in a very awkward position, but — with characteristic tact — he managed to save the situation.

Doubtless part of the reluctance to accept that *Bathybius* did not exist was the key role it played in the evolutionary theories of the time. Another reason was that Huxley was the most respected scientist of his day and — unlike Buchanan — widely liked. If you would like to know more about this remarkable man, read Box 3.1.

Box 3.1   Thomas Henry Huxley—a scientist 'worthy of all honour'

The Four Stages of Public Opinion

I (Just after publication)

The Novelty is absurd and subversive of Religion and Morality. The propounder both fool and knave.

II (Twenty years later)

The Novelty is absolute Truth and will yield a full and satisfactory explanation of things in general—The Propounder man of sublime genius and perfect virtue.

III (Forty years later)

The Novelty won't explain things in general after all and therefore is a wretched failure. The Propounder a very ordinary person advertised by a clique.

IV (A century later)

The Novelty is a mixture of truth and error. Explains as much as could reasonably be expected.

The propounder worthy of all honour in spite of his share of human frailties, as one who has added to the permanent possessions of science.

Huxley jotted down this aphorism in the early 1880s, twenty years or so after the publication of Charles Darwin's *The Origin of Species*, which he had championed against Bishop Samuel Wilberforce, in the famous debate of the British Association. At the time of the debate, Huxley was only thirty-five, sixteen years younger than Darwin, who by then was a scientist of high standing. Darwin had always intended that the worth of his book be judged by Joseph Hooker, the eminent botanist, Charles Lyell, the geologist, and Huxley himself. Although unwilling to come out publicly in favour of so subversive a theory, Lyell had effectively recognized the principle of natural selection through differential survival in the first edition of his *Principles of Geology*; Hooker was completely convinced by the arguments put forward in *The Origin of Species*, but Darwin nevertheless waited anxiously for Huxley's verdict. What was it about Huxley that made Darwin so value the support of one so much his junior?

Like many of his contemporaries, Huxley had come to science via medicine, but his career was far from commonplace. Despite only two years of formal schooling, at the age of seventeen he was awarded a Free Scholarship by Charing Cross Hospital; he went on to win prizes in chemistry, physiology and anatomy, and received a Gold Medal in the First Medical Examination of the University of London.

As a nineteen-year-old student he discovered a structure at the base of the human hair, and 'Huxley's layer' (as it is still known) became the subject of the first of his 150 published research papers.

When Huxley's Free Scholarship ended in 1846 he was some way off his full medical qualification. He decided that he must earn his living, and joined the Royal Navy as an Assistant Surgeon. Luckily, his unusual qualities were noticed and he was posted to HMS *Rattlesnake*, which was fitted out for an expedition to investigate the natural history of the South Seas. He was permitted to bring on board as many books as he liked and allowed free access to the chart room. He was also given introductions to several eminent scientists, including Edward Forbes, who showed him how to dredge up specimens at sea.

The expedition's official naturalist was mainly concerned with collecting specimens that could be preserved for display in museums, but Huxley—who became his unpaid assistant—was fascinated by the delicate, jelly-like organisms that came up in the dredge. In cramped, dark conditions, with his microscope lashed down against the rolling of the ship, he dissected and recorded creatures that had never before been properly examined, if at all. He was a skilful dissector, a talented artist and an accurate observer, and he drew what he saw. As a result, he could see organisms without being influenced by preconceived ideas, and he began to see flaws in the existing classifications, which had originated with the revered 'father of palaeontology', Georges Cuvier. At intervals during his four years on the *Rattlesnake*, Huxley sent packets of scientific papers home from ports-of-call. Such was the brilliance of these papers that by the time he finally disembarked at Chatham, not only was his academic career firmly established but he was a celebrity among the scientific community.

Despite the large number of animals he examined on the *Rattlesnake*, Huxley wrote on his return that he 'paid comparatively little attention to the collection of species, caring rather to come to some clear and definite idea as to the structure of those which had indeed been long known, but very little understood'. This approach—which he followed throughout his long and varied career—was the result of a great desire to come to grips with the larger picture; in the field of marine biology, this involved trying to establish where each organism fitted into the animal kingdom, living and extinct. When he described a fossil, he would not do so simply because it was new to science, but because it had a particular bearing on evolutionary theory or, perhaps, because a particular morphological feature showed a relationship with other fossil or living creatures. His ability to spot relationships and make connections was underpinned by an extraordinarily wide-ranging knowledge. In whatever field he was working, Huxley always tried to extract *general* principles from the example to hand. In this he was greatly aided by an ability to pick out from a mass of information the most significant aspects—to 'see the wood for the trees'.

When Ernst Haeckel (after whom Huxley was to name *Bathybius*) requested Huxley to obtain a place for him on a British government-funded expedition, Huxley wrote advising him as follows: 'I would counsel you to stay at home, and as Goethe says, find your America here … It is the organisation of knowledge rather than its increase which is wanted just now.' Huxley's passion for 'the organisation of knowledge' was not simply concerned with the individual elements of knowledge within specific disciplines, but encompassed whole fields of science. For example, he believed that the whole approach to the Earth sciences (a term not then in use) could be made more profitable: most geologists of the time were interested only in sedimentary rocks, almost for their own sake,

but Huxley felt that geology should be seen as 'the history of the earth, in precisely the same way as biology is the history of living beings', and he thought that to study stratigraphy (the Earth's 'anatomy') was insufficient: it was necessary also to study the processes occurring on and in the Earth (its 'telluric physiology') and their fundamental causes ('geological aetiology'). Like so much of Huxley's writing on scientific matters (as well as non-scientific ones), this approach seems remarkably modern.

It is impossible, here, to do justice to Huxley's enormous contribution to science and intellectual thought. However, we can provide a glimpse of it by simply listing his main achievements during 1868—the year in which he 'discovered' *Bathybius*. This was not an exceptional year, yet the number of scientific and educational projects he undertook seems almost unbelievable. He joined the commission on Science and Art Instruction in Ireland, was active in the British Association and the Royal Society, and in the Royal Society of Arts conference on Technical Education. He lectured at the Birmingham and Midland Institute, delivered an address 'On a Piece of Chalk' to the working men of Norwich, and began twelve years as honorary Principal of the South London Working Men's College.

His most publicized undertaking was a lecture delivered in Edinburgh one Sunday evening. Entitled 'On the Physical Basis of Life', it explained the idea (so intimately related to his deductions about *Bathybius*) that all living organisms consist ultimately of the same organic materials, together seen as making up 'protoplasm'. Taking this to its logical conclusion, he declared that 'the thoughts to which I am now giving utterance, and your thoughts regarding them, are the expression of molecular changes in that matter of life which is the source of our other vital phenomena'. The press interpreted the lecture as gross, mechanistic materialism, and condemned it with such vigour that, when published, it had to be reprinted six times!

In spite of the time devoted to public work, Huxley was determined to pursue his own private research. He continued to work in the fields of natural history, palaeontology and evolution, and was developing new interests in the anatomy and classification of birds and in anthropology and ethnology.

When Huxley died in June 1895, he left both science and education in a much better state than he found them. His legacies to future generations included not only the fruits of his prodigious research efforts and his innovative textbooks, but new institutions to promote and spread knowledge. Huxley lifted scientific thinking onto a plane it has seldom reached,

before or since, but he felt strongly that there should be no element of mystique about science. In his 1854 address 'On the Educational Value of the Natural History Sciences' he wrote:

Figure 3.5 Huxley the enthusiastic teacher and communicator, as portrayed in the magazine *Hornet* in 1871 (a year or so after he 'identified' *Bathybius*).

Science is, I believe, nothing but trained and organised common sense, *differing from the latter only as a veteran may differ from a raw recruit: and its methods differ from those of common sense only so far as the guardsman's cut and thrust differ from the manner in which a savage wields his club ... the vast results obtained by Science are* won by no mystical faculties, by no mental processes, other than those which are practised by every one of us, in the humblest and meanest affairs of life ... The man of science, in fact, simply uses with scrupulous exactness the methods which we all, habitually and at every moment, use carelessly. ■

Question 3.1 On the basis of what you have read in Box 3.1, which four of Huxley's attributes do you think contributed most to his success as a practising scientist?

3.3 'Bathysnap' and beyond

After the *Challenger* Expedition there was no longer any doubt that there was life on the deep sea-bed. Nevertheless, the sea-floor environment was still envisaged as hostile and unchanging, with deep-sea animals living slow, monotonous lives.

Question 3.2 Why might it be a mistake to label the deep sea—or indeed any 'unusual' environment (the polar regions, for example)—as 'hostile'?

Until well into the twentieth century, the deep sea was assumed to be a constant, unvarying environment: it was thought that the sea-bed was never disturbed by strong currents; that deep-sea temperatures never varied (at least not on short time-scales); and that the rain of fine sediment falling from above—clay and organic matter—arrived at a more-or-less constant rate, both spatially and temporally, regardless of what was occurring in surface waters.

One of the techniques that, over the last few decades, has prompted oceanographers to abandon some of these assumptions is deep-sea photography. Among the first oceanographers to use underwater photography in a systematic study of the deep-sea floor and its fauna was Bruce Heezen, of Lamont–Doherty Observatory. From the late 1940s until the 1970s, he and his group obtained hundreds of photographs (such as Figure 3.6), along transects of ocean floor, 'capturing' a variety of deep-sea organisms, some of which had never been seen before: there were the suspension feeders (for example sea-fans; see Figure 3.6b), filtering particles from the water column; various invertebrates feeding on the sediment surface, or burrowing and consuming it rather in the way that earthworms do (these are known as 'deposit-feeders'); and carnivores, such as octopi and crabs.

Activity 3.1

(a) On the basis of what you have been reading, from what must suspension-feeders and deposit-feeders in the deep sea obtain their nourishment?

(b) Look at Figure 3.6a and b. Which of the assumptions listed at the beginning of this section do they challenge, and why?

(c) What disadvantages does photography have for providing a full record of life on the sea-floor?

(a)

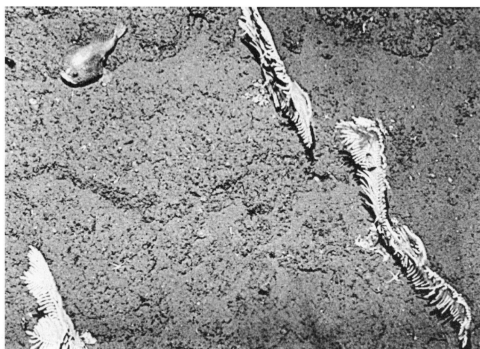

Figure 3.6 Just two of the many deep-sea photographs taken by Bruce Heezen and his colleagues. (a) The appearance of sediments at a depth of 1 000 m in the western equatorial Pacific (the object in the bottom left-hand corner is a compass). (b) Sea-fans (stalkless crinoids, about 30 cm high) and a fish; although difficult to see, there are basket stars entwined in the fronds of the sea-fans, and small white brittlestars on the sea-bed.

(b)

In the late 1960s, John Isaacs of Scripps Institute, California, deployed automatic cameras at depths down to 7 000 m. He used fish carcasses as bait and photographed them at intervals over the course of one or two days. The bait quickly attracted many large and highly mobile animals, including invertebrates and fish, and was consumed with astonishing speed. So much for the idea of a slow-living bottom population! What's more, such bursts of activity and feeding would occur every time a food bonanza arrived at the sea-floor, in the form of a dead fish, dead squid or dead marine mammal.

3.3.1   Is there spring in the deep sea?

We have just seen that even in the generally food-poor environment of the abyssal plains there are times and places where food is abundant. But what about the population explosions of phytoplankton that occur in surface waters in the spring as levels of sunlight rise? Could the effect of these **spring blooms**—and of the increased populations of zooplankton that feed on them—be transmitted to the sea-floor below, to stimulate a burst of springtime activity there?

You can begin to investigate this proposition in Activity 3.2.

Activity 3.2   *You should spend up to 30 minutes on this activity.*

The classical equation for the settling velocity, v, of a spherical object in a non-turbulent (that is, smoothly-flowing) fluid medium is:

$$v = \frac{1}{18} \, g \left(\frac{\rho_1 - \rho_2}{\mu} \right) d^2 \tag{3.1}$$

where g is the acceleration due to gravity,

d is the diameter of the particle,

ρ_1 is the density of the particle,

ρ_2 is the density of the fluid,

μ is the molecular viscosity—that is, the intrinsic 'stickiness' of the fluid (treacle, for example, has a very high viscosity),

and v is the settling velocity.

This relationship is known as **Stokes's law**.

(a) Phytoplankton (which are usually single-celled) vary in size between less than $2\,\mu m$ and $100\,\mu m$ ($1\,\mu m = 10^{-6}\,m$) in diameter; zooplanktonic organisms (many of which are single-celled) are mostly between about $100\,\mu m$ and several millimetres in diameter. As there are many more small plankton than large ones, you can take $10\,\mu m$ to be the diameter of a hypothetical 'typical' single-celled planktonic organism.

You know from Figure 2.16 that the density of seawater is about $1.03 \times 10^3\,kg\,m^{-3}$; assume that the density of a 'typical' plankton cell is about 2.2 times this. (This estimate is based on the fact that many plankton have shells or tests of silica or calcium carbonate, density 2.2–$2.5 \times 10^3\,kg\,m^{-3}$.) For seawater, $\mu = 10^{-3}\,N\,s\,m^{-2}$; $g = 9.8\,m\,s^{-2}$.

Use these data with Stokes's law (Equation 3.1) to estimate the settling velocity for our 'typical' plankton cell in $m\,s^{-1}$. How many days would it take the cell to fall from the surface to the sea-bed at a depth of $4\,000\,m$?

(b) Bearing in mind that horizontal current flow within the body of the ocean may be of the order of 0.1–$1.0\,m\,s^{-1}$, does it seem likely that plankton blooms in surface waters could have any effect on the organisms living on/in the sea-bed *directly* below?

(c) (i) Try to think of at least *two* reasons why Equation 3.1 is not really suitable for use in the situation we are considering. [*Hint* Imagine a radiolarian skeleton (Figure 2.6b) sinking down through the real (that is, not idealized) ocean.]

(ii) How else might you go about estimating the sinking rate of dead planktonic organisms?

(iii) Given what happens in the real ocean, why might our whole approach (that is, calculating how long it takes an individual plankton cell to sink to the bottom) be inappropriate?

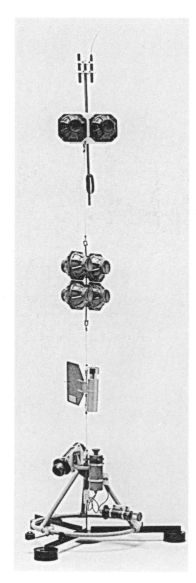

Figure 3.7 The Bathysnap rig. It consists not only of a camera and flash attached to a heavy tripod about 2 m high, but also a recording current meter, attached to the wire and kept taut by buoyancy spheres. At the end of the experiment, an acoustic signal causes the equipment to be released from the tripod; because of the buoyancy spheres it bobs up to the surface where it can be retrieved. (The photograph shows not the original rig deployed during the 1980s, but an improved version currently used by IOS oceanographers.)

In Activity 3.2 you have been exploring the kinds of ideas that were current up until the late 1970s: dead and dying phytoplankton, bodies of the zooplankton that fed on them, and faecal pellets of zooplankton and larger animals, all arriving at the sea-bed as a fine 'rain'. As these particles would have spent months or even years sinking through the water column, any correlation in time or space with their production in surface water would long since have disappeared, with the result that the supply of food to the deep sea would be constant and more or less evenly distributed over the sea-bed.

Then a programme of research involving sediment traps — funnel-shaped collecting vessels rather like rain gauges (Plate 3.1a) — began to produce results that challenged these ideas. Traps suspended in mid-ocean at depths of 2 000–3 000 m (though still some way off the bottom) were found to have collected very variable amounts of sinking organic debris, and the variations seemed to correlate closely in time (and space) with variations in the productivity of plankton in surface waters (Plate 3.1b). How could this be? The answer was supplied, a few years later, by deep-sea photography.

A team at the Institute of Oceanographic Sciences (IOS), UK, developed a device called 'Bathysnap', which would photograph the sea-bed repeatedly for periods as long as several months (Figure 3.7). In the early 1980s 'Bathysnap' was deployed in the Porcupine Sea Bight (see Figure 2.10a), a depression in the continental shelf to the south-west of Ireland, which is about 4 000 m deep and opens out onto the Porcupine Abyssal Plain. The results obtained were very exciting: although many of the animals had been seen before, they had never been observed in their natural habitat. Even the animals that live within the sediment — the 'infauna', which greatly outnumber the 'epifauna' (which live on the surface) — were 'captured' on film: some were recorded making occasional forays out on to the sediment surface; others were detected through the efforts of larger predatory animals to catch them by digging them up or ploughing up the sea-floor (Plate 3.2). Wyville Thomson and Carpenter, after whose vessel the chosen study region had been named, would have been delighted!

The photographs also recorded that certain animals were active at particular phases of the tide, apparently because they were responding to changes in tidal currents. This was particularly interesting because it suggested that sea-bed organisms might also respond to seasonal changes in bottom currents, particularly since such changes could bring water slightly warmer or cooler than usual (though still about 2 °C; see Figure 2.17). However, as far as the supply of food to the deep sea floor was concerned, no variability was detected at all — but in any case, that was not expected.

As it happened, for several years the IOS cruises to the Porcupine Sea Bight had taken place between October and April. Then, in 1981, 1982 and 1983, the cruises took place in May and July, and the situation observed was quite different. The time-lapse 'Bathysnap' pictures showed that the sea-floor would suddenly become covered with a dark, fluffy material (Plate 3.3) which, after a few weeks, would disappear. The suspicion that this fluff must be organic detritus resulting from the spring phytoplankton bloom was confirmed with the help of a specially designed sediment corer developed by the Scottish Marine Biological Association (SMBA). Using the SMBA corer, it was possible to retrieve samples of the fluff-covered sea-bed, completely undisturbed. When the fluff layer was examined under the microscope, it could clearly be seen to consist largely of decaying plankton (Figure 3.8). Furthermore, examination of sea-bed animals showed that they had been feeding on the material. The benthic foraminiferan shown in Plate 3.4a was collected from the Porcupine Abyssal Plain; inside its transparent body can be seen the green plant material it has just consumed — at a depth of 4 000 m this can *only* have originated in sunlit surface waters.

(a)

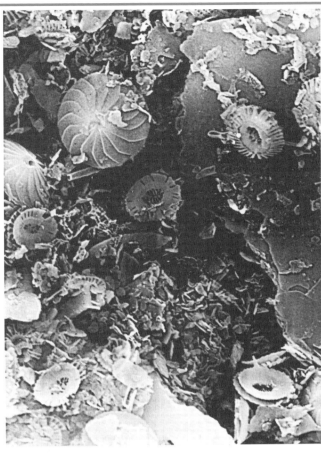

(b)

Figure 3.8 Photomicrographs of organic debris collected by a sediment corer from the sea-bed at a depth of 1 450 m in the Porcupine Sea Bight on 25 June 1985. (a) The topmost, undisturbed layer of fluff (magnification ×650): among the unidentifiable amorphous material can be seen the siliceous remains of diatoms (notably in the centre) and, much smaller, several coccoliths. (In the background can be seen the small holes of the filter used to separate the fluff from the fine inorganic sediment.) (b) Older detritus from the next layer down (magnification ×2 400), which contains a higher proportion of unidentifiable amorphous material, fewer siliceous remains but many more coccoliths (cf. Figure 3.3).

Given the timing of the spring bloom, this detritus must have sunk from surface waters in a matter of weeks, at speeds greater than 100 m day^{-1} — at least ten times faster than had been thought possible (cf. Activity 3.2).

It is now known that debris from plankton blooms aggregates into larger masses, which sink much faster than would be possible for individual cells (perhaps you thought of this possibility when doing Activity 3.2). These fluffy aggregates, known as 'marine snow', consist of dead and dying cells, living organisms (notably bacteria, which are the major 'food content' of the detritus as far as the benthic animals are concerned), and some inorganic matter (mostly clay particles); an individual 'snowflake' can be seen in Plate 3.5. Aggregation occurs partly because sinking particles tend to stick together if they touch. Another significant contribution comes from mucus 'nets', produced by small planktonic molluscs in order to trap food particles; when the 'nets' become clogged, they are abandoned.

So, there *is* spring in the deep sea, and indeed many benthic animals produce their young in time for them to take advantage of the springtime food bonanza. Furthermore, as a result of projects like Bathysnap and modern methods of sampling the deep sea-bed, some biological oceanographers now believe that the diversity of life in the deep sea may be as great as that in the tropical rainforests.

▷ Phytoplankton blooms in surface water represent CO_2 that has been 'fixed' from the atmosphere, through photosynthesis. Why might there be global significance in the unexpectedly high speed with which organic material produced in surface water sinks to the deep ocean?

▶ The sinking of phytoplankton and zooplankton (and their faecal pellets) from surface waters represents removal of 'greenhouse' CO_2 from the atmosphere into the deep ocean.

It is not known how important this 'biological sink' for CO_2 is in the context of the global carbon cycle. What is not in doubt, however, is that in mid-latitudes, in spring, large amounts of carbon dioxide pass from the atmosphere into the ocean.

3.3.2   Bathybius: 'a mixture of truth and error'?

▷ Compare Figure 3.4, the woodcut showing *Bathybius*, with Figure 3.8, the photomicrographs of 'marine snow' or 'fluff'. What points of similarity are there?

▶ Firstly, in both cases the material shown has an amorphous nature (and we also know that both can be described as somewhat gelatinous); secondly, both Figure 3.4 and Figure 3.8b show the material to contain little disk-like objects.

Huxley's own description of *Bathybius* as 'an irregular matter resembling white of egg, enclosing small bodies in shape somewhat of oval shirt studs' could well apply to marine snow.

▷ So what do you think the 'shirt studs' were?

▶ They are almost certainly coccoliths, the platelets of calcium carbonate which surround coccolithophores (and which can be clearly identified in Figure 3.8b). Whatever the origin of *Bathybius*, these platelets would probably be common in a sample of sediment from the sea-floor of the mid North Atlantic.

Interestingly, however, the samples of Atlantic mud in which Huxley first noticed *Bathybius* were collected in the springtime, as were the samples in which other people also identified it; by contrast, the *Challenger* samples, which lacked *Bathybius* (Section 3.2), were either collected at times and places where debris from a bloom would not, in any case, be likely, or were collected with equipment that would have destroyed it.

There is no doubt that some of the samples of *Bathybius* were simply inorganic substances that appeared during storage of the samples; Huxley certainly did not discover spontaneously generating protoplasm. But is it just possible that he was the first person to notice marine snow? If so, he was quite correct in identifying the 'amorphous matter' as being organic in origin. A century or so later, should we perhaps give our judgement on *Bathybius* as — to use Huxley's description (p. 30) — 'a mixture of truth and error'?

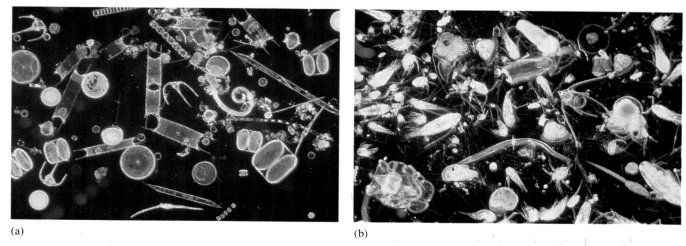

(a)   (b)

Plate 2.1   (a) Living phytoplankton, mainly diatoms and dinoflagellates; the field of view is about 1.75 mm across. (b) Living zooplankton, including copepods (planktonic crustaceans) and the planktonic larvae of various animals, including some benthic species; the field of view is about 1.75 cm across. Zooplankton may be herbivorous, feeding on phytoplankton, or carnivorous, feeding on other zooplankton.

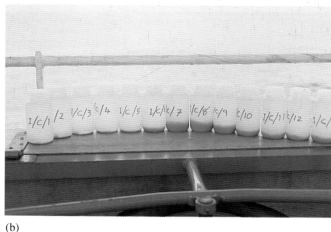

(b)

Plate 3.1   (a) A sediment trap being deployed from a research vessel. Beneath the 'funnel' is a rosette of bottles, which at predetermined intervals will click round to position a new bottle immediately below the funnel. This will enable the sediment collected to be 'dated' within a week or so, even though the trap may be left at sea for several months. (b) The bottles from a sediment trap deployed in the north-east Atlantic during spring and summer. The maximum production of organic debris, resulting from the spring phytoplankton bloom, can be clearly seen.

(a)

(a)

(b)

Plate 3.2 Time-lapse Bathysnap photographs on the Porcupine Abyssal Plain, showing holothurian (sea cucumber) life in the fast and slow lanes: (a) Two frames taken five hours apart catching the 'fast' holothurian *Oneirophanta mirabilis* on a single frame as it moves from top left to bottom right. (b) Two frames, also five hours apart, showing little movement in another type of holothurian; this animal had moved across the upper part of the frame from right to left, taking 22 days to cover about 1.2 m (see trail). Presumably, the fast holothurian has to select high-quality food to keep its 'fuel hungry' engine going, whereas the slower one can afford to ingest low-quality food, which stays in the gut for a long time. These photographs illustrate that, despite its limitations (see Activity 3.1 part (c)), deep-sea photography can provide important clues about how life is lived on the deep-sea floor.

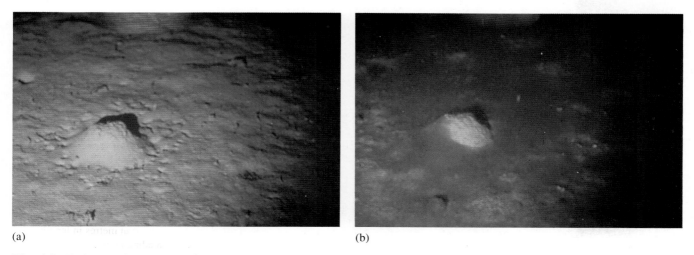

(a)   (b)

Plate 3.3 Bathysnap time-lapse photographs taken in spring 1983 at 4000 m on the Porcupine Abyssal Plain. Between 1 May and 15 June (a) greenish fluffy material begins to accumulate in hollows and around mounds; the one shown, made by an animal, is about 10 cm across. By mid-July (b), the sea-bed is almost covered with a carpet of 'fluff'. By mid-August the fluff has begun to disappear again.

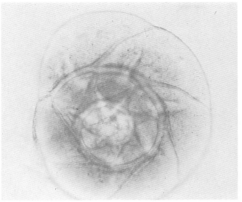

(a)

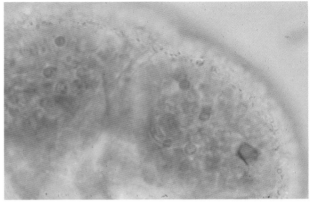

(b)

▲ *Plate 3.4* (a) A bottom-living foraminiferan, *Epistominella exigua*, extracted from phytoplankton debris, or fluff, collected from the Porcupine Abyssal Plain. The foraminiferan (which is 200 μm across) has been consuming green algal cells from the fluff. (b) Green algal cells (2 μm in diameter) seen through the transparent test wall of *E. exigua* (this specimen was collected from a depth of 4 550 m on the Madeira Abyssal Plain).

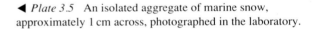

◄ *Plate 3.5* An isolated aggregate of marine snow, approximately 1 cm across, photographed in the laboratory.

Plate 4.1 Tube-worms — perhaps the most striking of the weird animals first seen at the Galápagos hydrothermal vent, some with their 'gills' protruding from the top of the red 'beak'. The tubes may be several metres in length. The small crab (bottom right) is feeding on bacteria covering the outsides of the tube-worms; it scrapes the bacteria off using its 'eye sockets', which no longer contain eyes, and have been adapted specifically for this purpose.

(a)   (b)

Plate 4.2 (a) A black smoker at 21° N on the East Pacific Rise. The hydrothermal fluid emerges from the chimney as a clear fluid at about 350 °C, but, on contact with cold, oxygenated bottom water, immediately precipitates minerals, building up the chimney and forming a black smoke of metal sulphides (plus oxides and hydroxides), which settle out onto the sea-floor. (b) Recently active hydrothermal 'chimneys', at a vent field at 26° N on the Mid-Atlantic Ridge. The chimneys are 1–2 m high; their predominantly yellow colouring indicates that they are built up from metal sulphides; the bluish material on the outside of some of the chimneys (especially the one near the front on the left) is anhydrite (cf. Figure 4.13). The blue anemones (bottom right) are characteristic of Mid-Atlantic Ridge vents.

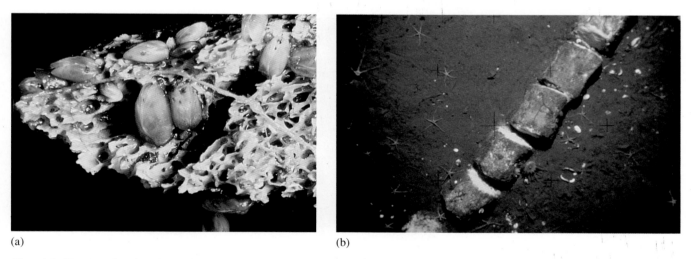

(a)   (b)

Plate 4.3 Photographs taken from *Alvin* of the half-buried remains of a whale (which was either a blue whale or fin whale) found in the Santa Catalina Basin. (a) Close-up of mussels nestling in an eroded rib-bone. The mussels are about 1 cm long, and are sustained partly through chemosynthetic bacteria. (b) The whale's vertebral column, seen from above (the vertebrae are about 40 cm long). The white spots on the sediment are clams, which have sulphide-oxidizing bacteria living symbiotically within them; sulphide-oxidizing bacteria were also found in the white bacterial mats which can be seen on the the ends of the vertebrae. (The anemone and the brittlestars covering the sea-bed are not part of the community that lives directly on the whale's skeleton.)

Summary of Chapter 3

1   The Mid-Atlantic Ridge is a spreading axis where hot magma rises to form new ocean floor. The sea-bed at ridge crests is very rough, but as new oceanic crust moves away from the axis, it cools and subsides, and becomes progressively covered by sediment. Eventually, the rough topography is completely blanketed by sediments: the resulting abyssal plains are the flattest regions on Earth and are 3–5 km below sea-level. (The rough topography of the crest and flanks of the Mid-Atlantic Ridge was not revealed by the relatively few depth soundings available to Maury in the 1850s.)

2   One of the greatest and most influential scientists of the nineteenth century was Thomas Henry Huxley. Arguably, Huxley's most important legacies to the scientific community were his efforts to get science 'organized', and his work in scientific education.

3   Huxley was not infallible. His two most important mistakes concerned the 'continuity of the chalk' and his 'discovery' of a single-celled organism (which he named *Bathybius*) covering samples of deep-sea mud. Most, if not all, samples of *Bathybius* were nothing more than hydrated calcium sulphate. Huxley's suggestion that the gelatinous substance was a mass of protoplasm was eagerly seized on by many scientists because it was thought that *Bathybius* might be the simplest possible organism from which all others have evolved. It is just possible that some samples of *Bathybius* — those collected in the springtime — were aggregates of marine snow (see point 4).

4   Since the 1940s, photographs taken on the sea-bed have been challenging many of our assumptions about the deep sea. We now know that conditions for life on the sea-bed are not constant: there are strong bottom currents and a variable food supply. Superimposed on the steady supply of fine organic debris from the photic zone are 'food bonanzas' — the carcasses of larger marine animals and, in mid-latitudes in spring, aggregates of debris from the plankton bloom, known as marine snow (or 'fluff'), which sinks down to the sea-bed in a matter of weeks. Benthic animal life consists of deposit-feeders and suspension-feeders (which depend on organic debris from the photic zone), and carnivores. Some biological oceanographers believe that the diversity of life in the deep sea may be as great as that in the tropical rainforests.

4 An alternative way of life

Pilot Jack Donnelly steered Alvin over black pillow lava. A long thin white plastic pole with a heat sensor on the tip swung out from *Alvin's* side … The digital temperature readout in the passenger sphere held steady at a normal 2 °C or 36 °F. The counter was rigged to beep with a thousandth of a degree temperature rise.

Within about fifteen minutes of touchdown at about 8 000 feet, the sensor beeped and the flashing red numbers indicated a hundredth of a degree rise in temperature. Suddenly *Alvin* was surrounded by life.

There were huge clamshells, stark white against the black elephant-skin basalt; brown mussels; a big bright red shrimp; a couple of white crabs scampering over the basalt; white squat lobsters; a brittlestar; a large pale anemone. … A many-legged creature pumped itself out of sight. Something sticking out of the bottom. Coral? A pretty little pale orange ball that looked like a dandelion gone to seed. Rocks covered in white streaks, what looked like pigeon droppings. Worms? A white crab… The water got foggy. Six of those white crabs. A whole cluster of those little peach-colored puffballs. And for as far as they could see, more clams and mussels—or were they oysters?—tucked in among the bulbous, black basalt. The hard earth, the basalt they had come for, was stained with the brilliant red and orange and ochre of iron sulfide—clearly the result of hydrothermal fluids. The basalt had been altered by heat, and for such young rocks, there was an extraordinary amount of alteration.

"We are sampling a hydrothermal vent", the shaggy-haired Corliss announced into the underwater telephone.

His graduate student Debbie Stakes … was surprised to hear of success so soon.

"Debra," Corliss said, 'isn't the deep ocean supposed to be like a desert?… Well, there's all these animals down here."

This passage comes from *Water Baby: the story of Alvin*, written by Victoria A. Kaharl of Woods Hole Oceanographic Institution in California. *Alvin* (Figure 4.1) is a direct descendant of Beebe's bathysphere and had come into being only after a long struggle on the part of the scientists and engineers who wanted to turn the dream of a small, manoeuvrable, deep-diving submarine—a 'submersible'—into reality. Coming up with the precise design specifications and putting these into practice had been no mean feat, but the hurdles that nearly proved insuperable were not, in fact, to do with problems of science or engineering, but with bureaucracy and, as we can see with hindsight, lack of scientific vision. For one thing, while not a ship in the usual sense, *Alvin* was expected to conform to the safety rules laid down for submarines; for another, her construction needed a funding go-ahead from the US Navy, and the Navy saw no strategic advantage in possessing submersibles. Finally, practically the only US oceanographers who believed that there would be significant scientific value in observing the deep-ocean environment at first hand was the small group who had been developing *Alvin* at Woods Hole.

Eventually, however, on June 5, 1964, the deep-diving submersible was officially commissioned. The champagne bottle was broken against the mechanical arm by Adelaide Vine, wife of Al Vine, a geophysicist who, with vision and determination, had probably done more than most to bring the submersible into being. It was not by

Figure 4.1 Alvin at the start of a dive. Within the outer hull is a titanium passenger sphere, just big enough to hold three people in discomfort. Unlike conventional submarines, Alvin is very manoeuvrable and can dive deeper than 4 000 m (see Figure 4.2). The size of Alvin can be gauged from the diver on the left.

chance that it had acquired the name *Alvin*; unfortunately there were those in authority who were not amused that the impressively engineered piece of hardware had the same name as a cartoon chipmunk!

4.1 A FAMOUS adventure

The event described in the quotation occurred in 1977; it is possible that funding for *Alvin* would have dried up some years before this, were it not for a deep-sea project that arose as a result of political will rather than scientific initiative. In 1967, the United States Marine Council, a cabinet-level advisory board to the President (then Lyndon Johnson), recommended a second international Law of the Sea Conference to build on the work started by the first conference in 1958.

The Marine Council proposed that, in order to encourage a spirit of international cooperation, the United States should initiate joint oceanographic projects with other countries. So was born the idea for FAMOUS, the French–American Mid-Ocean Undersea Study—a project in which deep-diving submersibles would be used to study a section of the Mid-Atlantic Ridge. At that time, the theories of **plate tectonics** and **sea-floor spreading** (Figure 3.2) had been accepted by most Earth scientists, but it was not known how exactly new sea-floor is formed at spreading ridges; the idea was to examine the sea-floor close up, much as geology is carried out on land—not simply collecting rock samples but studying the relationships of rocks one to another.

FAMOUS received the official go-ahead in July 1972, and it was agreed that the French would use their bathyscaph *Archimède* and a small deep-diving submarine *Cyana*, while the Americans would use *Alvin*. Unfortunately, *Alvin* was suffering from wear-and-tear and technical problems, and though the French made some initial dives in the summer of 1973 it was not until June 1974 that the project began in earnest.

A study area was chosen some 640 km south-west of the Azores (Figure 4.3a), and a number of novel techniques were used to survey and record the area. Underpinning

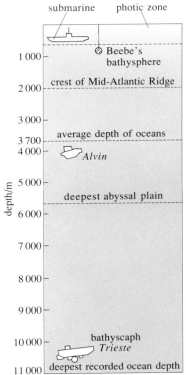

Figure 4.2 Schematic diagram showing the depth capabilities of *Alvin* and various other underwater vessels in relation to ocean-floor topography. The first successful 'untethered' vessel was August Piccard's 'bathyscaph' *Trieste*, launched in 1953. It worked on the same principle as a balloon: it sank because of several tonnes of ballast, which was detached when the time came to ascend. In 1960 the *Trieste* descended into the Challenger Deep in the Mariana Trench; discovered in 1952 by a combination of traditional sounding methods and echo-sounding, the Challenger Deep remains the deepest known feature on the face of the Earth.

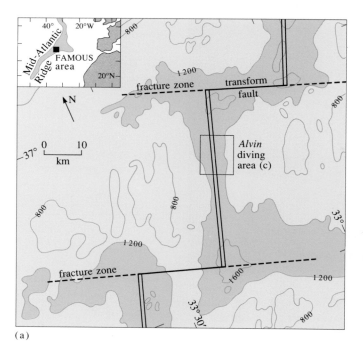

(a)

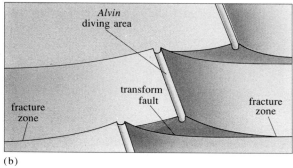

(b)

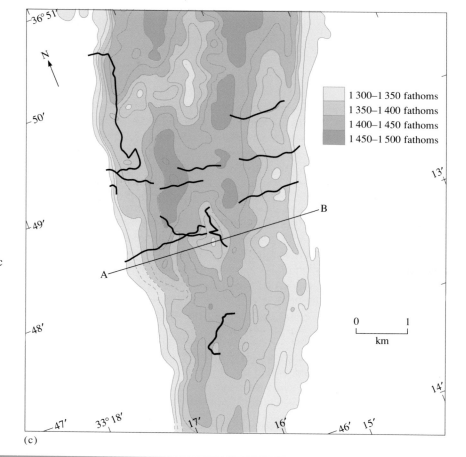

(c)

Figure 4.3 (a) Bathymetric map of part of the section of Mid-Atlantic Ridge surveyed at the start of the FAMOUS project, with depths in fathoms; the inset shows the general location of the area on the Mid-Atlantic Ridge. The straight black lines are an interpretation of the bathymetry in terms of a spreading ridge or constructive plate margin (parallel lines) offset by **transform faults**, whose extensions either side of the ridge are **fracture zones** (dashed lines). (b) Sketch interpretation of the central part of the map in (a) (*not to scale*). (c) A more detailed bathymetric map of the area selected for closer examination by submersible. The black squiggly lines show submersible tracks.

all of these was an extremely precise navigational system, which made use of acoustic *transponders* (*trans*mitters that re*spond* to a signal from the surface) placed on the sea-bed and 'linked' to both the submersibles and their support ships (*Alvin*'s support ship was *Lulu*). Precise position-fixing would be essential—mapping is all but meaningless if you don't know where you are, and surveying in the FAMOUS project needed to be accurate to within 10 m or so.

A 'sound picture' of the sea-bed topography was obtained using both a narrow beam echo-sounder (conventionally downward looking, but producing high-resolution images) and a British side-scan sonar system known as *GLORIA* (cf. footnote on p. 26). Part of the FAMOUS study area was then selected for further investigation by *Archimède, Cyana* and *Alvin.* A preliminary survey of this area produced the bathymetric map shown in Figure 4.3c.

Activity 4.1

(a) In three or four sentences, referring to specific depths as appropriate, *describe* the sea-bed topography suggested by the contours in Figure 4.3c, remembering that they show *depths* below sea-level in fathoms.

(b) *Sketch* the general shape of the sea-floor along the line A–B in Figure 4.3c. What do you think the feature in the centre of your sketch might be?

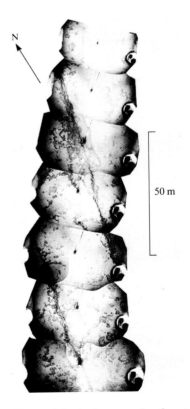

During FAMOUS, underwater photography of the sea-floor was used to much greater advantage than ever before. A specially developed camera system, with a very powerful light, was towed above the sea-floor. Successive pictures were taken, so that photomosaics of intermediate-scale features could be built up. Figure 4.4 shows part of the floor of the **axial rift valley**, the valley identified in Activity 4.1.

Although the photomosaics were very useful, they did not prepare the oceanographers for what they were to see with their own eyes and photograph through *Alvin*'s tiny portholes. It was like 'driving in first gear through a light snowfall at night', but the scenery they saw was dramatic and unexpected. The west wall of the rift valley, in particular, loomed up steeply, while between the volcanic hills the valley floor was criss-crossed with crevasses and faults (Figures 4.4 and 4.5c); the faults were indications that the sea-floor was being pulled apart. On a smaller scale, the sea-bed was no less dramatic. The flanks of the volcanoes were made up of bulbous lava formations, known as **pillow lavas** (Figures 4.5a and 4.6).

Given the widespread evidence of volcanic activity, and what was understood about the underlying cause of sea-floor spreading (Figure 3.2), the FAMOUS oceanographers believed that somewhere in the rift valley they would find unusually warm water emerging from the sea-floor. It was presumed that seawater seeping down through cracks and fissures in the ocean crust would become heated by the same magma chambers that had produced the abundant pillow lavas. Being heated, the percolating water would become less dense and rise again (that is, would convect), to escape at the sea-floor. Such **hydrothermal activity** (but involving heated groundwater) is found in volcanic areas on land, and some of its most spectacular manifestations are the hot springs and geysers of Iceland, which straddles the Mid-Atlantic Ridge.

Figure 4.4 A photomosaic of part of the rift-valley floor surveyed in the FAMOUS project, showing two of the numerous fissures that run parallel to the valley walls. (Note how the scale compares with that in Figure 4.3c.)

Figure 4.5 Some of the photographs of the rift-valley floor taken through *Alvin*'s porthole: (a) a pillow lava and *Alvin*'s sampling arm; (b) numerous pillow lavas, with a thin veneer of sediment; (c) a fissure (cf. Figure 4.4) cutting through pillow lavas with a covering of sediment. The field of view is about 1 m across for (a) and 3 m across for (b) and (c).

(a)

(b)

(c)

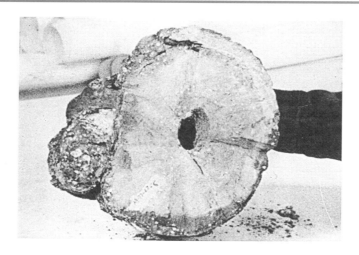

Figure 4.6 A section through a lava pillow, about half a metre in diameter, collected in the FAMOUS area. Note the glassy 'rind' around an interior made up of small crystals.

Figure 4.6 shows a lava pillow collected from the FAMOUS area. Its interior is **crystalline**—made up of interlocking crystals—but its outermost skin has a **glassy texture**.

▷ What does this imply about the cooling of the molten lava?

▶ It implies that the outermost 'skin' of the lava cooled so fast that it was 'quenched', forming a glass because there was no time for crystals to form. Once sealed in its glassy rind, the interior of the pillow could cool more slowly, allowing crystals to form.

The fact that the outsides of lava pillows cooled almost instantaneously suggested to the *Alvin* scientists that the continuous flow of cold (2–3 °C) seawater was sufficient to carry away enormous amounts of heat without itself being warmed significantly. This in turn suggested that it might be very difficult to detect water that had been warmed by circulating through hot oceanic crust.

It was thinking along these lines that led the scientists on one of the *Alvin* dives to decide to explore a narrow crevasse or fissure where warm water could have been trapped, and protected from mixing significantly with the bottom seawater. No warm water was found and, worse, *Alvin* became wedged in the crevasse. It took two hours for the pilot to extricate the craft, a feat that was only possible because the two scientists had noted the direction of the prevailing current and carefully observed the shape of the fissure before entering it.

From a fissure near to the one in which *Alvin* became stuck, the French oceanographers collected samples of basalt that were streaked with red, yellow and green. Analysis showed that this basalt contained much less cobalt and copper than the samples that had been collected previously; furthermore, the basalt's veneer of sediment contained an unusually large proportion of iron and manganese. It seemed likely that this basalt had been chemically altered through contact with hot seawater, so that the composition of both the seawater and the rocks had been altered; the iron and manganese in the sediments were presumed to have been supplied by the same hydrothermal activity.

The existence of hydrothermal activity in oceanic crust was not proved or disproved during the FAMOUS expedition. But by the time the lava flows had been carefully mapped it was clear that the mechanism whereby sea-floor spreading occurs at mid-ocean ridges was not at all the neat and simple production of new sea-floor that had been imagined. FAMOUS had proved the value of going down to see the deep sea-bed at first hand.

4.2 Getting warmer ...

FAMOUS was a great success, both scientifically and as a demonstration of the viability and value of using submersibles to investigate the deep ocean. Nevertheless, for *Alvin* the financial climate remained very cold. This was the time of the Vietnam war, and the US Navy, traditionally a supporter of ocean-related research, could no longer direct resources towards oceanography. Much of the burden for the funding of oceanography shifted to the National Science Foundation (NSF), but this could not even keep the academic research fleet at sea.

Research vessels began to be laid up, some for ever, and oceanographic centres began to fight for survival. In such an atmosphere what chance was there for the idiosyncratic *Alvin*? The very success of FAMOUS was now used against the submersible by those who claimed that it was useful only to a narrow group of marine geologists and geophysicists.

In the end, it was agreed that the NSF, NOAA (National Oceanic and Atmospheric Administration) and the Navy would jointly fund *Alvin*. The deep-diving submersible was saved, but its role had to change; it would no longer be the preserve of the Woods Hole scientists, but would become a national facility, available to the whole US oceanographic community. Proposals for dives would be vetted by a review committee, of which the Woods Hole representative was only one of twelve.

With this new national role, *Alvin*'s tasks became more varied. During 1975 and 1976 there were scientific dives deep into the Cayman Trough, off the Bahamas and off the coast of California. The submersible was used by the Navy to investigate beneath a Soviet trawler (the *Alvin* crew found only empty Russian sardine tins), and to retrieve a piece of classified equipment which had fallen into the sea. There were also investigations into a dump site in the Atlantic, 190 km off Delaware. The site was supposed to be for general rubbish and low-level radioactive waste, but the *Alvin* dives revealed that many drums of radioactive waste had never reached the site, but had been dumped closer inshore; those that had made it there were so corroded that most of the waste had already leaked out.

4.2.1 Clambake, Eden, Dandelions and Oyster Beds

As we have seen, the FAMOUS project provided exciting new information about processes occurring at spreading axes. However, even at the time FAMOUS was launched, it was already known that spreading axes are not all the same. The wide axial rift valley, which provided the setting for FAMOUS, is very characteristic of the Mid-Atlantic Ridge. In contrast, the spreading ridges in the Pacific — the north–south trending East Pacific Rise, and the east–west trending Galápagos spreading axis (Figure 4.7), have less well-developed axial rift valleys and, furthermore, have considerably less rugged topography. These topographic differences result from the fact that the rates of sea-floor spreading in the Atlantic are significantly lower than those in the Pacific. Sea-floor formed at the Mid-Atlantic Ridge is moving away from it at a spreading rate (strictly, half-spreading rate) of $1–2\,\mathrm{cm\,yr^{-1}}$ (that is, the Atlantic basin is widening by $2–4\,\mathrm{cm\,yr^{-1}}$). In the Pacific, half-spreading rates are $6–8\,\mathrm{cm\,yr^{-1}}$ for the East Pacific Rise and $3–4\,\mathrm{cm\,yr^{-1}}$ for the Galápagos spreading axis.

▷   In the light of the above, how would you explain why, having failed to find evidence of heated seawater at the FAMOUS site, marine geologists began to make plans for *Alvin* to dive at a Pacific spreading axis?

At fast-spreading ridges like those in the Pacific, hot magma would be likely to be rising up to supply magma chambers at a greater rate than at slow-spreading ridges. It would therefore be reasonable to suppose that the heat supply to spreading ridges in the Pacific would be greater than at the Mid-Atlantic Ridge, and evidence of hydrothermal circulation might more easily be found.

In fact, some indications of hydrothermal activity on the Galápagos spreading axis had already been found in 1972. A few hundred kilometres to the east of the Galápagos Islands (Figure 4.7), thermometers towed above the sea-bed had recorded small temperature anomalies (that is, values significantly different from normal): $\approx 0.1\,°C$ for the bottom water, and a few times this for the bottom sediment. Furthermore, echo-sounding traces of the sea-bed included strange 'fuzzy' regions. Some scientists thought these were caused by masses of super-hot water near the sea-bed; others thought they were echoes from mounds about 15 m high.

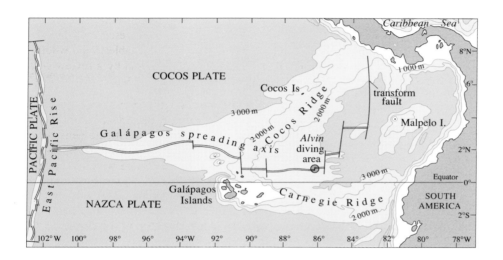

Figure 4.7 Plate-tectonic setting of the eastern equatorial Pacific. The blue circle shows the *Alvin* diving area.

In 1976, two more scientific expeditions to investigate the Galápagos site found similar indirect evidence for hydrothermal activity. On the basis of these results, the NSF agreed to fund *Alvin* to dive at the site in February of the following year. The press announced the planned dives as follows:

SCIENTISTS TO EXPLORE HOT SPRINGS AT BOTTOM OF PACIFIC TO LEARN HOW METAL-RICH SEDIMENTS ARE FORMED

Scientists will dive to the bottom of the Pacific Ocean in a 22-foot, three-man submersible in February to explore for the first time vents in the sea floor through which metal-bearing hot waters flow.

The findings are expected to help scientists understand the formation of metal-rich deep sea sediments, the history of the chemistry of sea water and the transfer of heat from the earth's interior into the oceans.

Dr John B. Corliss, assistant professor of oceanography at Oregon State University, the project coordinator, said the expedition's findings could determine whether hot springs could some day have economic value …

"We'll have to proceed with caution to avoid exposing the submarine to waters that are very hot," Corliss said. "We'll be working with unknowns. No one has ever seen these things up close …"

The US public could not know that John Corliss was only describing, with great confidence, what he *thought* he would find!

On arrival at the Galápagos study site, the oceanographers began by dropping navigational transponders, similar to those used during FAMOUS, onto the sea-floor. One set, known as Faith, Hope and Charity, were dropped close to the peculiar 'mounds' revealed on the sonar. Another set — Sleepy, Dopey and Bashful — were dropped in the vicinity of the highest temperature anomaly; this area was known as the 'Clambake', because sea-bed photographs showed that it had more than average numbers of clam shells.

In advance of *Alvin*'s dives, the study area was surveyed by means of *'ANGUS'*. Developed for use in FAMOUS, this *A*coustically *N*avigated *G*eological *U*ndersea *S*urveyor was dragged along the sea-bed, with its camera taking a picture every ten seconds and its temperature sensor recording variations in temperature. As in 1976, the temperature record showed small anomalies; furthermore, Kathy Crane, a graduate student, noticed that the anomalies *always* occurred where unusually large numbers of clam shells could be seen on the sea-bed. She was assured by a senior scientist that these must be the remains of a clambake on a passing ship.

But the senior scientist was wrong. The quotation at the beginning of this chapter describes what *Alvin*'s crew saw when, on the first dive, they headed for the Clambake site and the highest temperature anomaly: not only did they find a **hydrothermal vent**, where water heated in the crust emerged at the sea-floor, but bathed by the warm water were strange animals, including giant clams. However, the connection between the warm water and the animals was not at all clear.

The following day, *Alvin* took the scientists to the area where the sonar had indicated the presence of large mounds, or perhaps extremely hot water. Instead of mounds they found tall pinnacles, resembling stalagmites; the temperature of the bottom water was normal, there were no clams and, indeed, no unusually prolific fauna whatsoever.

The oceanographers suspected that the stalagmites, which were streaked with yellow, purple and green, were made not of basalt but of metal sulphides. This suspicion was strengthened the following day when *Alvin* returned to the Clambake to collect some of the strange animals and some water samples. When, back up at the surface, a water bottle was opened, the smell that filled the ship was the repulsive 'rotten eggs' odour of hydrogen sulphide, H_2S.

Some of the animals from the Clambake were like nothing anyone had ever seen before. As described in the quotation on p.40, there was a fluffy-headed creature like a dandelion gone to seed, 'puff-balls', and white eyeless crabs. Yet more strange creatures were found at a nearby vent site, which became known as the Garden of Eden; the most striking of these were large worms which stood upright in flexible white tubes, waving red plumes (Plate 4.1); yet another vent site became known as the Dandelion Patch because there were so many of the fluffy-headed creatures.

The question was: 'What was supporting so many animals so far from the sunlit surface layers?' One theory was that the 'updraft' of the warm waters from the vents drew in such large volumes of water from the surrounding sea-bed that the area had more than its share of organic 'fallout' from the surface. This idea was dismissed, however; there were so many large animals — megafauna — around the vents that the community could not possibly be supported in this way.

The answer was in the sulphide. The red and white tube-worm was found to have sulphide-oxidizing bacteria in the equivalent of its gut, and its red 'beak' turned out to be like gills, but capable of extracting not only oxygen but hydrogen sulphide from seawater; the clams and mussels were found to have sulphide-oxidizing bacteria in their gills, and so on. These bacteria were clearly living within the animals *symbiotically* — that is, so that both the bacteria and the host animals were benefiting. It was deduced that the chemical energy released by the oxidation of hydrogen sulphide (and of other sulphides and methane) is used by the bacteria to reduce CO_2 to organic molecules such as carbohydrates, in the same way that light energy is used by plants to fix carbon from CO_2 (Figure 4.8): the bacteria are using **chemosynthesis** rather than photosynthesis.

Activity 4.2

Study Figure 4.8, which compares a hydrothermal vent ecosystem, driven by the energy released through the oxidation of sulphide by bacteria, with the 'conventional' photosynthetic ecosystem, which is driven by sunlight (Figure 4.8a). The photosynthetic equation is the same one that you wrote down for Question 2.1.

(a) Complete and balance the equation printed in blue in Figure 4.8b to show how sulphide-oxidizing bacteria can also 'fix' CO_2 (originally dissolved in seawater) to produce carbohydrates (along with sulphate (SO_4^{2-}) and hydrogen (H^+) ions as by-products).

(b) Explain *why* the bacteria are described as sulphide-oxidizing.

PHOTOSYNTHESIS WITHIN GREEN PLANTS

$$6CO_2 + 6H_2O \xrightarrow{\text{sunlight}} \underset{\text{carbohydrates}}{C_6H_{12}O_6 + 6O_2}$$

CHEMOSYNTHESIS BY SYMBIOTIC BACTERIA

$$6CO_2 + 6H_2S + 6O_2 + 6H_2O \xrightarrow{\text{chemical energy}}$$

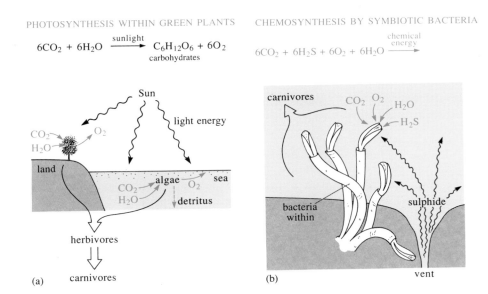

Figure 4.8 Comparison of a hydrothermal vent ecosystem (represented here by a group of tube-worms) driven by sulphide-oxidizing bacteria with an ecosystem driven by sunlight. In (a) the energy for the production of carbohydrates comes from the Sun (photosynthesis); in (b) the energy for carbohydrate production comes from sulphide-oxidizing bacteria (chemosynthesis).

It turned out that, although the symbiotic bacteria were the main food producers, there were also two other types of bacteria using the sulphide: 'plume' bacteria, living within the vent waters, and mat-forming bacteria, which covered the rocks and animals in the vicinity of the vent. The plume bacteria are a food source for suspension-feeding zooplankton, and the mat-forming bacteria are 'grazed' by animals like snails and shrimps; all of these animals support carnivores, including fish and lobsters. Since the discovery of the Galápagos **warm-water vents**, a number of other vent communities have been found, some living around vents gushing hydrothermal fluid considerably hotter than that seeping out of the sea-bed at the Clambake. Oceanographers were not surprised to find these extremely hot vents. You will see why in the next section.

4.2.2 Warm-water vents lead to black smokers

During the course of *Alvin*'s exploration of the Galápagos vent field, numerous samples of water were collected from around the vents. One of the scientific questions that the scientists hoped the samples would help to answer was: what part does hydrothermal circulation play in helping to balance the ocean's budget of chemical constituents?

As you know (Box 2.3), most of the ocean's dissolved constituents are supplied by rivers. For most elements, if we estimate the mass supplied each year in river water and the mass removed each year into sea-floor sediments, the figures are more or less the same; in other words, the rate of addition of dissolved constituents is balanced by their rate of removal from solution. As a result their concentrations do not change with time, and the oceans are said to be in a **steady state**.

But things are not that simple; consider the element manganese, for example. From estimates of the volume of river water entering the oceans each year and of the average concentration of manganese in river water, it has been calculated that about 10^5 tonnes of manganese are supplied to the oceans each year by rivers. However, from analysis of sea-floor sediments it has been estimated that between 4×10^6 and 6×10^6 tonnes of manganese are *removed* into sediments each year — about 50 times as much as is supplied by rivers!

▷   What is the implication of these figures, given that the average concentration of manganese in seawater remains the same?

▶   There must be another source of manganese for the oceans.

As hinted above, it was thought that hydrothermal activity would prove to be the 'missing source' for manganese; another element that needed an extra source was calcium. On the other hand, the mismatch between supply and removal of magnesium and sulphate (SO_4^{2-}) implied that these constituents must have a 'sink' in addition to removal into sediments. Again, this might be explained by hydrothermal activity.

It was known that hot seawater reacts with basalt to produce new minerals; the colourfully streaked rocks seen during the FAMOUS expedition were evidence for this. So also were hydrothermally altered rocks found in ophiolite complexes. The exchange of ions between ocean-floor rock and hot seawater had also been demonstrated by laboratory experiments using powdered basalt, which showed in particular that while the seawater gained iron, copper and nickel (as well as manganese), it lost sulphate and magnesium; it seemed probable that hot seawater reacting with basalt for a sufficiently long time would lose all of these two constituents.

Water samples obtained by *Alvin* during the Galápagos dives did indeed provide answers to some of the conundrums concerning the concentrations of certain ions in seawater. But that was not all. Shortly, you will have the opportunity to use data from water samples collected by *Alvin* to see for yourself how the existence of the most dramatic features of the deep-sea floor was predicted before they had ever been seen in action.

Figure 4.9 shows data for samples of water collected from close to the vents at the Clambake, Dandelion Patch, Oyster Beds and the Garden of Eden (all within a few hundred metres of one another). In Figure 4.9, the concentration of sulphate ion, $[SO_4^{2-}]$, has been plotted against the concentration of silica, $[SiO_2]$, for 28 samples (the square brackets [ ] indicate 'concentration of'). The fact that the points lie more or less in a straight line indicates that the samples plotted are all mixtures, in various proportions, between two bodies of water — one with a relatively high SO_4^{2-} concentration and a relatively low SiO_2 concentration, the other with a relatively low SO_4^{2-} concentration and a relatively high SiO_2 concentration. The line along which the points plot is known as a **mixing line**.

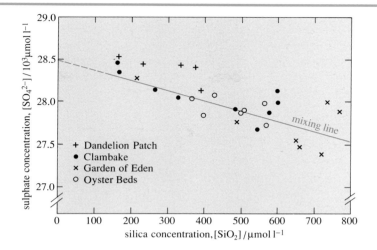

Figure 4.9 Plot of sulphate concentration against silica concentration for different samples of water collected close to vents. Crosses represent samples of water from the Dandelion Patch, filled circles are samples from the Clambake site, etc. (This graph and those in Figure 4.11 come from a scientific paper published by the *Alvin* scientists and their colleagues in 1979.)

If you find the idea of a mixing line puzzling, look at Figure 4.10, which shows a mixing line between two bodies of water, W_1 and W_2: one of them has a high concentration of constituent B and a low concentration of constituent A, and the other has a low concentration of constituent B and high concentration of constituent A. All mixtures of W_1 and W_2 have concentrations of A and B which are intermediate between those of neat W_1 and neat W_2; they therefore lie along the mixing line.

▷ Where would a mixture of equal parts W_1 and W_2 plot? And where would a mixture containing 95% W_1 and 5% W_2 plot?

▶ Both mixtures would plot on the mixing line. The one with equal parts W_1 and W_2 would plot half-way along the mixing line (and would have concentrations of A and B midway between those of W_1 and those of W_2). The one containing 95% W_1 would have concentrations of A and B very close to those of W_1 and would therefore plot on the mixing line very close to W_1. To be precise, it would plot 95/100 of the way along the line towards W_1.

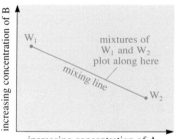

Figure 4.10 A mixing-line diagram, showing mixing between two bodies of water W_1 and W_2, which have differing concentrations of two constituents, A and B. W_1 and W_2 are sometimes referred to as the *end-members* of the mixing line.

If you look at Figure 4.9, you will see that samples of water collected from different locations contained different concentrations of sulphate and silica. This was despite the fact that water collected from close to the vents had not had time to mix with the 'local' bottom water. The *Alvin* scientists concluded that the water emerging from the sea-floor was in fact different mixtures of 'neat' hydrothermal fluid and seawater which had permeated down into the oceanic crust. (Note that the end-members, W_1 and W_2, corresponding to the neat hydrothermal fluid and seawater, have not been plotted on Figure 4.9.)

If a physical property of a body of water can only be changed by that water *mixing* with other water for which that property is different, then that property can be treated like constituent A or B in Figure 4.10 and used in mixing-line diagrams. Temperature is one such property, and is the obvious property to use for the study of mixtures of cold seawater and hot hydrothermal fluid. Unfortunately, a problem with the sampling technique meant that the temperature measurements were rather imprecise. However, when temperature was plotted against silica concentration for a large number of samples (Figure 4.11a), a mixing line was obtained which was sufficiently reliable for the temperature of a sample to be determined on the basis of its silica content (you will see how this worked in a minute).

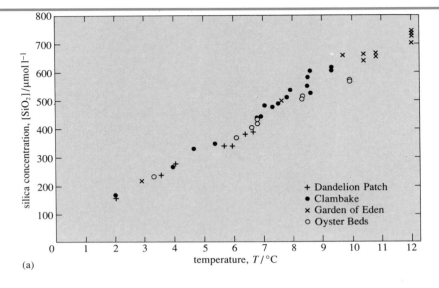

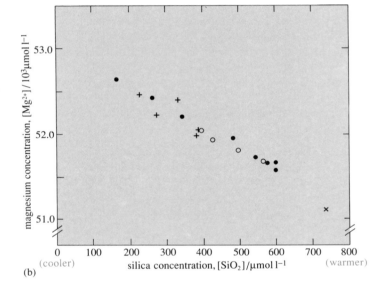

Figure 4.11 Plots of (a) silica concentration against temperature, and (b) magnesium concentration against silica concentration, for different samples of vent waters. The relationship between $[SiO_2]$ and temperature shown in (a) enables $[SiO_2]$ data to be used as a proxy for temperature.

▷ Look at the T–$[SiO_2]$ mixing line in Figure 4.11a. Does the proportion of hydro-thermal fluid in the samples increase from right to left or left to right? What can we deduce about the amount by which the fluid has been diluted by the time it emerges at the sea-bed?

▶ The temperature of the samples increases from left to right so the proportion of hydrothermal fluid in the water must increase from left to right. However, there are no samples warmer than 12 °C—nowhere near the temperature of rock in the vicinity of a magma chamber—so the hydrothermal fluid emerging at the sea-bed must be *very* dilute.

▷ How does Figure 4.11a support the assumption that it is ordinary seawater that is mixing with hydrothermal fluid in the crust?

▶ There are no samples colder than 2 °C—the temperature of deep ocean water.

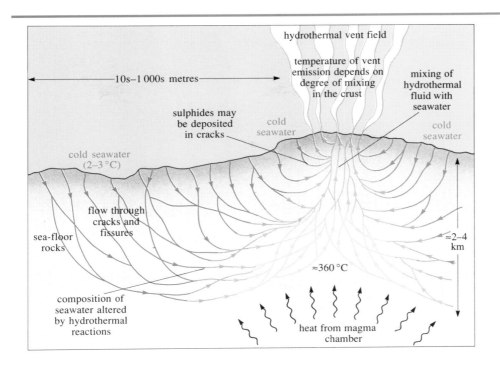

Figure 4.12 Schematic diagram to illustrate hydrothermal circulation, showing how hot hydrothermal fluid may become mixed with seawater before emerging at the sea-bed at warm-water vents.

Figure 4.12 illustrates what was envisaged to be occurring. Hydrothermal fluids originate as ordinary seawater, which circulates through the oceanic crust, heating up and exchanging ions with the rock as it goes, so that its composition (and that of the rock) changes. If it circulates for a sufficiently long time it eventually reaches chemical equilibrium with the rock: its composition stops changing, and it has become our 'neat' hydrothermal fluid. However, as the hydrothermal fluid rises towards the sea-bed, it mixes with a much larger volume of seawater which has locally percolated down through cracks and fissures; mixtures between hydrothermal fluid and local seawater are substantially cooler than the neat fluid, and have compositions closer to that of normal seawater. It is these mixtures that are represented by the data points on Figure 4.9 and Figure 4.11.

By using mixing diagrams like those in Figure 4.9 and Figure 4.11, the *Alvin* scientists and their colleagues demonstrated that during hydrothermal circulation seawater loses all its magnesium and sulphate to the hot oceanic crust, and gains from it large amounts of manganese, calcium, lithium and rubidium (among other elements). At the same time, they deduced the temperature of neat hydrothermal fluid, prior to mixing with cold seawater. If you would like to do the same, you should do Activity 4.3 (otherwise, go straight to the text at the end of the activity).

Activity 4.3   *You should spend up to 30 minutes on this activity.*

Look back to Figure 4.9, the $[SO_4^{2-}]$–$[SiO_2]$ plot. (Remember that we are using $[SiO_2]$ simply as a means of estimating the temperature.) The best-fit mixing line through the data points was actually determined by computer. The line represents an equation of the form

$$y = mx + c$$

where y is the variable plotted on the vertical axis (in this case the sulphate concentration, $[SO_4^{2-}]$), x is the variable plotted on the horizontal axis ($[SiO_2]$), and m is the gradient of the line. Thus, in terms of the variables involved, the equation of the best-fit line is

$$[SO_4{}^{2-}] = -1.2[SiO_2] + (28.5 \times 10^3)\,\mu mol\,l^{-1} \qquad (4.1a)$$

▷   What is the significance of the $+ (28.5 \times 10^3)\,\mu mol\,l^{-1}$? And why is the gradient written with a minus?

▶ $(28.5 \times 10^3)\,\mu mol\,l^{-1}$ is the intercept of the line with the $[SO_4{}^{2-}]$ axis — that is, the value of $[SO_4{}^{2-}]$ when $[SiO_2] = 0$. The gradient is written with a minus because the line has a *negative* slope; that is, it slopes down to the right, so that higher values of $[SO_4{}^{2-}]$ correspond to lower values of $[SiO_2]$.

Now it's your turn—without the benefit of a computer!

(a) Following the steps used above for the sulphate data in Figure 4.9, obtain the corresponding equation for the magnesium data in Figure 4.11b. This will be in the form

$$[Mg^{2+}] = A[SiO_2] + B$$

Let us call this second equation, Equation 4.1b.

If you aren't happy with your Equation 4.1b, have a look at the answer without reading past the broken line.

You should now have two equations, one relating $[SO_4{}^{2-}]$ to $[SiO_2]$ and the other relating $[Mg^{2+}]$ to $[SiO_2]$.

▷   On the assumption that continuous hydrothermal reaction eventually removes all sulphate and magnesium from seawater, what do we do now if we want to know the temperature of neat hydrothermal fluid?

▶   We need to discover what the temperature would be for a sample containing *no* seawater and hence with no sulphate or magnesium. In other words, we need to know what temperature would correspond with $[SO_4{}^{2-}] = 0$ and $[Mg^{2+}] = 0$. To do that, we first have to find out what $[SiO_2]$ value(s) correspond(s) with $[SO_4{}^{2-}] = 0$ and $[Mg^{2+}] = 0$.

As you have no doubt noticed, the $[SO_4{}^{2-}]$ and $[Mg^{2+}]$ axes on Figure 4.9 and Figure 4.11b do not extend continuously down to zero. This is not a problem, however, because we have our two Equations 4.1a and 4.1b. We can use them to find out what $[SiO_2]$ value(s) correspond to $[SO_4{}^{2-}] = 0$ and $[Mg^{2+}] = 0$.

Putting $[SO_4{}^{2-}] = 0$ in Equation 4.1a, we get

$$0 = -1.2[SiO_2] + (28.5 \times 10^3)\,\mu mol\,l^{-1}$$

Rearranging,

$$[SiO_2] = \frac{28.5 \times 10^3}{1.2}\,\mu mol\,l^{-1}$$

$$= (23.8 \times 10^3)\,\mu mol\,l^{-1}$$

So, when $[SO_4{}^{2-}] = 0$, $[SiO_2] = (23.8 \times 10^3)\,\mu mol\,l^{-1}$.

(b) Use your Equation 4.1b to determine the $[SiO_2]$ value that corresponds to $[Mg^{2+}] = 0$. Is the answer what you expected?

(c) Take the average of the $[SiO_2]$ values corresponding to $[SO_4{}^{2-}] = 0$ and $[Mg^{2+}] = 0$.

(d) Use the average [SiO_2] value that you have just calculated to find out the temperature of undiluted hydrothermal fluid, given that the equation for the best-fit mixing line for the temperature–[SiO_2] plot is:

$$[SiO_2] = 62.5T + 93.8 \, \mu mol \, l^{-1} \qquad (4.2)$$

You have now followed the same thought processes and, hopefully, come up with the same answer as the *Alvin* scientists themselves.

The scientific paper from which Figures 4.9 and 4.11 have been taken was submitted for publication in the journal *Earth and Planetary Science Letters* in February 1979. One of its authors was John Corliss, who had been in *Alvin* when the first warm-water vents were discovered (see the quotation at the beginning of this chapter). As we mentioned earlier, the main purpose of the paper was to attempt to quantify the importance of hydrothermal circulation in adding and removing elements to and from solution in seawater. At the same time, however, the authors demonstrated that the temperature of undiluted fluid must be about 360 °C: if hydrothermal fluid could somehow reach the sea-bed without mixing with cold seawater within the ocean crust, this is approximately the temperature at which it would emerge. Vents gushing extremely hot fluid (≈350 °C) were indeed found later the same year (1979) at 21° N on the East Pacific Rise, a spreading axis near the mouth of the Gulf of California (see Figure 4.14). These vents were **black smokers**—chimneys made mainly of sulphides of iron, copper and zinc, out of which billowed a smoke of black sulphide particles (Plate 4.2).

Ironically, the scientists in *Alvin* did not at first realize the significance of what they had found. When they saw the first smoker, they moved in on it so that *Alvin*'s sample basket could break the top off the chimney. The 'smoke' belched out all the more, and the PVC rod bearing the temperature probe was placed in it by means of *Alvin*'s pincers. No-one in the submersible realized what a dangerous thing they were doing. The highest temperature recorded at the Galápagos vent field had been 23 °C, and the temperature probe had been calibrated to be accurate between 0 and 25 °C; John Corliss was alone in wanting it to be accurate up to 100 °C. As it happened, on the momentous occasion of finding the first smoker, the temperature probe was not working properly and recorded 32 °C. However, back at the surface, the PVC rod was seen to be blackened, and to have melted at the tip. It was only then that some of the scientists realized how rash they had been: the melting temperature of PVC is 180 °C. Other scientists remained sceptical, but in subsequent dives *Alvin* found five other sets of belching chimneys, and the probe showed that the temperature of the black 'smoke' was about 350 °C.

Even more ironically, the smokers had narrowly missed being discovered the previous year. A group of French and American scientists diving on the East Pacific Rise in *Cyana* had found strange mounds and stacks, similar — had they but known it — to the 'stalagmites' of metal sulphides found at the FAMOUS site. A piece of a mound was broken off and, after a brief inspection, packaged for transportation to France. It was six months later that a visiting American geologist saw it and realized that it was sulphide. Ruefully recalling the failure to spot the significance of the mounds, the French geologist Jean Francheteau remarked 'One wears blinkers in the ocean'.

▷ The metals in the sulphide stalagmites had been largely leached from the oceanic crust. Given that hydrothermal fluids are reducing, what do you think was the origin of the sulphide ions?

▶ They must be derived from sulphate ions (SO_4^{2-}) in seawater, which were reduced to sulphide ions (S^{2-}).

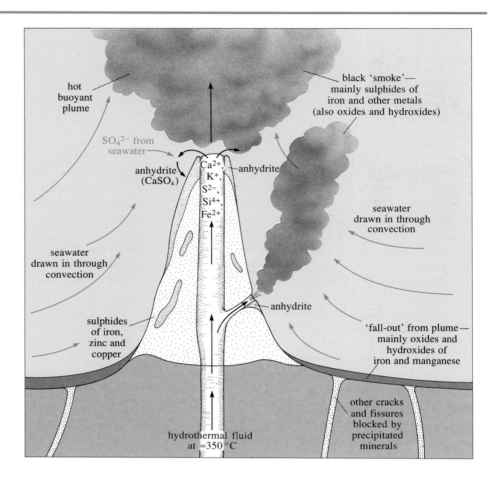

Figure 4.13 Cross-section through a black smoker. The reason the smoker forms in the first place is that the precipitating minerals — including sulphides, anhydrite ($CaSO_4$) and silica (SiO_2) — have blocked up most of the cracks through which seawater could percolate down to mix with the rising hydrothermal fluid (cf. Figure 4.12). Precipitation continues on the sea-floor, so that a chimney builds up around the vent.

Figure 4.13 is a schematic cross-section through a black smoker.

▷ By reference to Figure 4.12, try to suggest why hydrothermal fluid billows upwards out of black smokers, instead of flowing out gently like the fluids at warm-water vents.

▶ As shown in Figure 4.13 (and discussed in the caption), most of the cracks at black smokers have been blocked up by precipitating minerals. This prevents local seawater from percolating down to mix with the rising hydrothermal fluid. As it has not been significantly diluted, the fluid at the sea-bed is close to its original temperature, and is therefore of considerably lower density than the ambient seawater. It is because it is extremely buoyant that it billows out so dramatically.

It is worth mentioning that in addition to being chemically reducing, undiluted hydrothermal fluid is considerably more acidic than seawater. Despite this, black smokers support abundant animal life, some of which lives in close proximity to the emerging fluid.

Since 1979, warm-water vents, black smokers and — intermediate between the two — 'white smokers' (which produce clear fluid or white precipitates, comprising notably barium sulphate), have been found in a variety of plate-tectonic settings (Figure 4.14). Each vent area has its own fauna, a particular distinctive combination of vent animals — all more or less bizarre — which may nevertheless resemble that at the nearest group of vents, perhaps many hundreds of kilometres away.

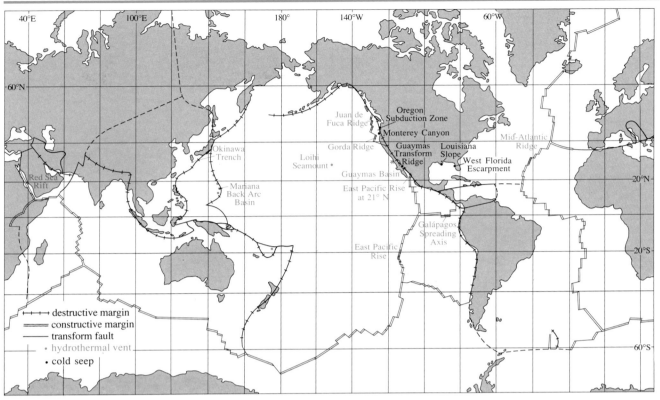

4.3 Whales as stepping-stones

One of the problems that has interested people studying vent fauna is *how* the animals manage to spread from one group, or 'field', of vents to another, given the large distances of cold, food-poor (especially for them) bottom waters that separate one field from another. The ability to spread to other vents would seem to be especially important because vents are ephemeral. The cold, dead chimneys seen at the Galápagos indicated that vent fields do not last long on the geological time-scale; we now know that individual vents are only active for a few decades, and groups of vents only for a thousand years or so.

▷ How do you think vent animals can spread, given that many of them produce planktonic larvae?

▶ The larvae will be transported in currents, and a small proportion of them will end up in the right kind of environment.

The question is, what is the 'right kind of environment'? In 1987, scientists diving in *Alvin* made a fascinating discovery at a depth of 1 240 m in the Santa Catalina Basin off California (see Figure 4.14). It was a complete whale skeleton, about 60 m long; this was surprising because whales that die in shallow waters (such as the North Sea) float as a result of gases evolved during decay, and their carcasses gradually break up. It was deduced that the whale died at depth, with the result

Figure 4.14 Hydrothermal vents have now been discovered in a variety of plate-tectonic settings (including spreading ridges and transform faults) as well as in mid-ocean situations like the (volcanic) Loihi Seamount. This map also shows the location of 'cold seeps' where anoxic organic-rich sediments emit methane and hydrogen sulphide, which support animals related to vent fauna; some of these sediment accumulations occur along continental margins and others in the deep trenches at subduction zones (destructive plate margins). Broken lines indicate uncertainty in the plate margins. The fact that long lengths of plate boundaries do *not* have vents or cold seeps marked on the map probably simply indicates that no-one has yet been to look for them. The star marks the location of the 'whale fall' site discussed in the next section.)

that high hydrostatic pressure prevented it from floating to the surface and breaking up. However, the completeness of the skeleton was not the greatest surprise; this came when a bone collected for further examination was found to reek of hydrogen sulphide.

Large carcasses always decay anaerobically because their small surface area : volume ratio means that the bulk of the tissue cannot be reached by oxygen diffusing in from outside.

▷ Remembering back to Section 4.2, what does the presence of hydrogen sulphide suggest about how decay could proceed?

▶ It could proceed through the action of sulphide-oxidizing bacteria.

Returning to the whale carcass the following year, the *Alvin* scientists found that some bone surfaces were indeed covered by mats of sulphide-oxidizing bacteria; furthermore, the bones were also supporting a number of animals, including mussels and limpets (which carried methane-oxidizing bacteria) and two species of giant clam — all characteristic of hydrothermal vent environments (see Plate 4.3). It seems that the hydrogen sulphide and methane (which at vents are supplied in hydrothermal fluid) were being produced during the final stages of decomposition of fats within the bone.

So, the carcasses of whales and other large marine animals can provide 'stepping stones' for vent species — sulphide-rich oases between one hydrothermal environment and the next. Luckily, we have not yet reached the point where the deep sea has ceased to surprise us.

4.4 Postscript

Over the course of a century and a half our perceptions of the deep sea have changed dramatically: from an environment totally hostile to life it became a monotonous, unchanging place where life was lived at a slow and steady pace. Through deep-sea photography, this view was challenged, even before warm vents and hot smokers were discovered, but now some of us have seen with our own eyes the astounding variety, activity and productivity that is supported by an energy source other than the Sun.

But what of the other great debate that has run in parallel with the speculations about the deep sea — that concerning the origin of life itself? It may have struck you that life could have begun with bacterial chemosynthesis in the deep sea. Indeed, there are some good reasons to think it may have done. Individual vent fields may be very short-lived, but there must have been environments of this type in the deep sea since the oceans first formed some 4000 million years ago. So, while individual communities may not have lasted long, their progeny will always have been able to find a similar environment in which to carry on the species. Conditions at deep-sea vents may have changed considerably less than conditions at the surface and on land, where climatic variations can be most felt. Some of the organisms at vents are indeed very primitive — 'living fossils' that Wyville Thomson would have dearly loved to see. Perhaps the deep sea really is the 'cradle of creation' after all.

Summary of Chapter 4

1   The American deep-diving submersible *Alvin* was developed as a result of the foresight and determination of a small group of scientists who believed that if the deep ocean floor is to be understood it needs to be observed at first hand. The scientific value of deep-diving submersibles was first proved during the FAMOUS project, when close-up examination of a section of the axial rift of the Mid-Atlantic Ridge provided important clues to the volcanic processes that accompany sea-floor spreading.

2   Although indications of past hydrothermal activity were observed during the FAMOUS project, water warmed by circulating through hot oceanic crust was not found. However, in 1977, warm-water vents were discovered in the Pacific, on the (fast-spreading) Galápagos spreading axis. Also found — but not identified — were the chimneys of extinct black smokers (see point 4).

3   During hydrothermal circulation, heated seawater reacts with hot oceanic crust, with the result that the compositions of both are changed. In particular, seawater loses magnesium and sulphate (which is converted to sulphide), and gains (among others) iron, manganese, silicon and calcium. Hydrothermal activity thus provides the extra 'source' (in the case of, say, manganese) or 'sink' (in the case of, say, magnesium) needed to 'balance the books' for supply and removal of various elements in seawater.

4   At warm-water vents, the rising hydrothermal fluid mixes with seawater that has percolated down into the oceanic crust, with the result that the water that emerges at the sea-bed is only slightly above ambient temperature, and has a composition fairly close to that of ordinary seawater. However, by means of mixing-line calculations, it was possible to predict the temperature (≈ 350–$380\,°C$) and (to some extent) the composition of undiluted hydrothermal fluid; these predictions were borne out in 1979 when black smokers were found on the East Pacific Rise. In black smokers, the rising hydrothermal fluid is isolated from 'local' seawater because the cracks in the crust are blocked by the precipitation of metal sulphides and other minerals. Precipitation continues on the top of the crust, building up the characteristic 'chimneys'.

5   The emissions from hydrothermal vents support prolific and exotic faunas, whose primary energy source is the chemical energy released by sulphide-oxidizing bacteria. Some larger vent organisms live symbiotically with the chemosynthetic bacteria, some feed directly on them, and yet others are carnivores. Similar communities have been found at 'cold seeps' and living on whale bones; carcasses of large marine mammals could provide 'stepping stones' for vent species. Life may have begun with bacterial chemosynthesis in the deep sea.

Question 4.1   During the FAMOUS project, the close-up observations were undertaken using photography, but the large-area surveys were carried out using different types of echo-soundings. In two or three sentences explain why the two different approaches were necessary.

Question 4.2   Which of the photographs (a)–(c) in Figure 4.5 do you think shows the oldest lavas and which the youngest? How can you tell?

Activity 4.4

Read Extract 4.1. On the basis of what you have read in this chapter, what do you think about the possibilities put forward in the article?

Extract 4.1   From *The Independent*, 2 July 1992.

Life found deep beneath the earth

By Steve Connor, Science Correspondent

SCIENTISTS have discovered live bacteria several miles below ground that have apparently lived off energy from the Earth's core for millions of years. Other researchers have previously reported microbes living at about 200 metres below the seabed, but this is the first time that live bacteria have been discovered at great depths in ancient granite rock.

The discovery of the deepest living organisms could upset existing theories on the origin of life, which invoke the importance of the Sun's energy in sustaining organisms. Unlike life-forms on the surface of the planet, the subterranean bacteria seem not to have relied on the Sun's energy for their survival. They could be a model for possible underground life on other planets, Thomas Gold, emeritus professor of astronomy at Cornell University, New York, said yesterday.

The amount of life existing deep underground could exceed that living on or near the Earth's surface, he said. "We do not know at present how to make a realistic estimate of the subterranean mass of material now living, but all that can be said is that one must consider it possible that it is comparable to all the living mass at the surface ... There are certainly very major life-forms down there."

There are at least ten other planets or their moons in the Solar System where similar subterranean microbes could exist, he said.

Ulrich Szewzyk, a microbiologist at Sweden's National Bacteriological Laboratory in Stockholm, has cultured several strains of new bacteria from samples of granite rock taken from a borehole at depths of between five and six kilometres, Professor Gold says in the current issue of the *Proceedings of the National Academy of Sciences*.

The borehole was drilled in an ancient crater in central Sweden called the Siljan Ring, caused by the impact of a massive meteorite millions of years ago. Because the rock is granite, and not sedimentary deposits such as sandstone, it is unlikely the microbes originated from life on the surface, Professor Gold said. The bacteria do not need oxygen and live at very high temperatures of about 100 °C.

Dr Szewzyk has written a "very substantial" scientific paper on the discovery and, co-operating with Carl Woese, Professor of Microbiology at the University of Illinois, will submit it later this year to the US National Academy of Science for publication.

Activity 4.5

It is often held that science and common sense are closely linked. Thomas Henry Huxley ... spoke of science as being nothing more than trained common sense ... However reasonable they may sound, such views are, alas, quite misleading.

This is how Lewis Wolpert, a Professor of Biology and writer on science, begins the first chapter of his book *The Unnatural Nature of Science*.

On the basis of what you have read in this book and in the Course as a whole, do you agree with Huxley or with Wolpert?

Further reading

Those books published before 1990 are (or could well become) out of print; however, all can be obtained via your local library.

Bibby, C. (1972) *Scientist Extraordinary: the Life and Scientific Work of Thomas Henry Huxley 1825–95,* Pergamon Press.

Concise, readable account of Huxley's life and work.

Deacon, M. (1971) *Scientists and the Sea: 1650–1900: a Study of Marine Science,* Academic Press.

Classic account of the development of oceanography, set in its historical context.

Hamilton-Paterson, J. (1992) *Seven-tenths: the Sea and its Thresholds,* Hutchinson.

Not a scientific textbook, but the author's personal exploration of humanity's relationship with the sea; idiosyncratic, and often philosophical, it provides an additional perspective to much of the material in this book.

Heezen, B.C., and Hollister, C.D. (1973) *The Face of the Deep,* Oxford University Press.

This large book (descibed by the authors as an 'illustrated natural history of the visible abyss') consists mainly of (black and white) photographs of sea-floor animals. Although it was written while knowledge of the deep sea was still very limited, it nevertheless provides a useful and accessible introduction to various aspects of oceanography.

Jones, I., and Joyce J. (1992) *Oceanography in the Days of Sail,* Hale & Ironmonger (UK distributors: Turnaround Books).

A lively account of the growth of physical oceanography in the eighteenth and ninetenth centuries. The emphasis is on the historical circumstances and the (sometimes colourful) personalities of the protagonists, but there are also some interesting descriptions of scientific technniques and instrumentation.

Kaharl, V. A. (1990) *Water Baby: the Story of Alvin,* Oxford University Press.

Written by the 'Science Writer in Residence' at the Woods Hole Oceanographic Institution, this entertaining account is intended to be accessible to readers with little or no scientific background, but it nevertheless provides insights into the scientific aims of the *Alvin* team, as well as into the politics and personalities surrounding *Alvin*'s development.

McConnell, A. (1982) *No Sea Too Deep: the History of Oceanographic Instruments,* Hilger, Bristol.

The illustrations of the original instruments are fascinating, and along the way the reader discovers a considerable amount about the development of oceanography.

Schlee, S. (1973) *A History of Oceanography: the Edge of an Unfamiliar World,* Robert Hale.

Enthusiastic account of the development of oceanography from the middle of the last century up until the 1960s. Particularly interesting is the contrast between the evolution of the science in the United States and its evolution in Europe and, especially, Britain (as discussed in this book).

Wolpert, L. (1992) *The Unnatural Nature of Science*, Faber & Faber.

The author's idiosyncratic and thought-provoking response to the question: 'is science merely trained common sense?'. Perhaps a good way to round off *Science Matters*!

Wyville Thomson, C. (1873) *The Depths of the Sea: an account of the general results of the dredging cruises of HMS 'Porcupine' and 'Lightning' during the summers of 1868, 1869 and 1870.* Macmillan and Co.

Fascinating for the insight it provides into the scientific thinking of the time, and for its discussion of the work undertaken on the voyages.

The following articles from scientific journals should also be of interest:

Lampitt, R. (1985) Fast living on the ocean floor, *New Scientist,* 28 February, pp. 37–40.

Article about the early Bathysnap work, concerning the evidence for 'Spring in the deep sea' and describing feeding strategies on the deep sea floor; also includes a short piece on early underwater photography.

Two issues of *Oceanus* (the popular journal produced by Woods Hole Oceanographic Institution) largely devoted to hydrothermal vents and the communities that depend on them:

'Deep-sea hot springs and cold seeps', *Oceanus,* **27** (3), Fall 1984.

'Mid-ocean ridges', *Oceanus,* **34** (4), Winter 1991/92.

Skills

In this section we list skills that have been explicitly taught and/or revised in this book. You will find that most of them are special instances of the general skills categories given in the *Course Study Guide*. After each one there is a list of questions and activities where that skill is practised.

1   Express a chemical reaction in terms of a balanced chemical equation. (*Question 2.1; Activity 4.2*)

2   Make an estimate of a physical property by substituting the appropriate values into an algebraic formula. (*Question 2.3; Activities 2.1, 3.2 and 4.3*)

3   Extract information from or interpret text, photographs, contour maps, graphs (including mixing diagrams) and cross-sectional diagrams (particularly those illustrating dynamic processes). (*Questions 2.3 and 4.2; Activities 2.3, 3.1, and 4.1–4.4*)

4   Use scientific understanding and imagination to envisage the consequences of a particular physical situation. (*Questions 2.1 and 2.4; Activities 2.1–2.3, 3.1 and 3.2*)

5   Consider personal, social and political factors that may influence the rate of growth of scientific understanding. (*Questions 2.2 and 3.1; Activity 4.5*)

Answers to questions

Question 2.1

Vegetables, that is to say, plants, depend on photosynthesis—the synthesis of organic compounds using the energy of sunlight—for growth. Only the uppermost part of the ocean is sufficiently well lit to allow marine plants (either seaweeds growing on the sea-bed or small floating algae known as phytoplankton) to photosynthesise. (This sunlit layer—the **photic zone**—is about 200 m deep in the open ocean, less in turbid coastal waters.)

During photosynthesis, plants take up CO_2 (which in the case of marine plants is taken up from solution in seawater) and combine it with the hydrogen in water to produce carbohydrates. The equation you may have thought of is:

$$6CO_2 + 6H_2O \xrightarrow{\text{sunlight}} \underset{\text{carbohydrates}}{C_6H_{12}O_6} + 6O_2$$

Question 2.2

A possible modern parallel has arisen with space flights—the early stages of space exploration. It could be argued that the main purpose of such flights—particularly the early manned flights undertaken by the United States and the former Soviet Union—was the boosting of national prestige, or one-upmanship. (Even the recent *Voyager* missions have been criticized for concentrating too much on producing images for publicity purposes, at the expense of science.) Perhaps you thought of other examples.

Question 2.3

The hydrostatic equation is $P = \rho g z$. We are ignoring variations with depth of temperature and salinity, and hence density (ρ), so the pressure at any depth (z) is directly proportional to z. The variation of P with depth will therefore be a straight line. If we make the simplifying assumption that 10 m of water is equivalent to about 1 atmosphere or $\approx 10^5$ N m^{-2}, the straight line will be the black broken line on Figure 2.23. More accurately, using 1.03×10^3 kg m^{-3} as the average density of seawater, the pressure at a depth of 10 000 m would be $(1.03 \times 10^3) \times 9.8 \times 10\,000 \approx 1\,009 \times 10^5$ N m^{-2}, and the variation of P with depth will be given by the solid black line on Figure 2.23. If you had included the effect of compressibility, the graph would have had a slight curve on it, as shown schematically by the blue line in Figure 2.23. (In reality the diference would be too small to show up on the scale of Figure 2.23.)

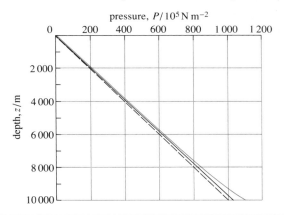

Figure 2.23
Answer to Question 2.3.

Question 2.4

When retrieved, the 'minimum' marker of the thermometer would record that the thermometer had been in water of about 3.75 °C — the lowest temperature encountered between the surface and a depth of 2 000 m. In fact, the temperature at 2 000 m is higher than this, nearer to 4 °C. In other words, there is a 'temperature inversion', with colder water overlying warmer (possible because of the differing salinities of the water masses involved — see the in-text question following Box 2.3).

As they did not appreciate the role of salinity in determining the density of seawater, or know the complexity of the deep circulation, Ross and his contemporaries assumed that temperature always increased with depth in the ocean, down to the top of the 4 °C 'reservoir'.

Question 3.1

You would have been justified in selecting any of Huxley's attributes given below:

o   an impartial and accurate observer;

o   an ability to see relationships and spot connections;

o   determined and hardworking;

o   an ability to see the wood for the trees;

o   a desire to come to grips with the larger picture;

o   capable of admitting when he was wrong;

o   wide-ranging scientific knowledge.

Question 3.2

It could well be argued that whether an environment is hostile depends very much on what, or who, you are. For organisms adapted to an environment it is the very opposite of hostile. We humans tend to judge the hostility of an environment with respect to ourselves, which means that we tend to assume that life is 'difficult' in, for example, very cold (or indeed, very hot) conditions. A creature adapted to life in the deep sea would be likely to find the surface environment inimical.

Question 4.1

For close-up observations, photography is clearly very useful, *provided* that there is a strong light source (see the answer to Activity 3.1c). However, as light is strongly absorbed and scattered by seawater, there can be no submarine equivalent of aerial photography. Sound, on the other hand, travels through seawater with very little loss of energy, and is ideally suited for use in large-scale surveys of the sea-bed. (Remember that marine mammals can communicate through sound across thousands of kilometres.)

Question 4.2

Figure 4.5a shows the youngest lava and Figure 4.5c the oldest. You can tell this because whereas the pillow lava in (a) has, as yet, no covering of sediment, those in (b) have 'a thin veneer' and those in (c) are largely concealed by the sediment. Sediment rains down continually, so the longer the lava has been at the sea-floor, the more sediment it will carry (assuming that the sediment hasn't been redistributed by 'landslides' or bottom currents).

Answers to activities

Activity 2.1

(a) (i) Using $P = \rho g z$, the pressure at a depth of $3\,700\,\text{m}$ is given by:

$$P = (1.03 \times 10^3)\,\text{kg m}^{-3} \times 9.8\,\text{m s}^{-2} \times 3\,700\,\text{m}$$
$$= 37\,300 \times 10^3\,\text{kg m}^{-3}\,\text{m s}^{-2}\,\text{m} \; (\equiv \text{kg m s}^{-2}\,\text{m}^{-2})$$
$$= 3.7 \times 10^7\,\text{N m}^{-2}$$

(ii) Hence, $3\,700\,\text{m}$ of seawater give rise to a pressure equivalent to approximately $3.7 \times 10^7/10^5 = 3.7 \times 10^2 = 370$ atmospheres.

So at a depth of $3\,700\,\text{m}$, the pressure is ≈ 370 atmospheres. Therefore ≈ 10 metres of seawater gives rise to the same pressure as one atmosphere (1 bar). This relationship is very useful to oceanographers who need to know the depth at which samples are taken, temperatures measured, etc. Oceanographic instruments often carry pressure sensors that record the pressure in decibars (1/10 bar), which to a first approximation corresponds to the depth in metres.

(b) (i) We have been assuming that seawater is incompressible (or nearly so), so that ρ can be regarded as constant. If it were very compressible, water at depth would be compressed by the water above it to such an extent that ρ would increase markedly with depth. The total weight of water overlying a square metre of sea-bed would therefore be significantly higher than we assumed in part (a), and, as a result, so would the pressure; see Box 2.2. (We could still use the hydrostatic equation, by using a depth-averaged value for ρ, which would be higher than ρ at atmospheric pressure.)

(ii) The fact that the density of seawater increases only slightly with depth means that the increase of pressure with depth is nothing like that imagined by the early Victorians. It certainly doesn't result in the bottom waters of the ocean being 'heavier than molten gold'!

Activity 2.2

We cannot know for sure how Ross had reasoned, but, given the belief in the $4\,°\text{C}$ maximum density of seawater, it must have been along the lines of the following (don't worry if you didn't get this):

At higher latitudes than the 'circle of mean temperature', surface waters could be cooled to $39.5\,°\text{F}/4\,°\text{C}$ (and below). Once cooled to $4\,°\text{C}$ it would be denser than underlying water (unless that were also at $4\,°\text{C}$) and would sink, displacing less dense water, which would rise to the surface until it, too, were cooled to $4\,°\text{C}$ and sank in turn (see Box 2.2). Over the course of millenia, the deep ocean would fill up with water of $4\,°\text{C}$; even when surface conditions were colder than this, the temperature of the deep 'reservoir' would be unaffected.

At latitudes lower than the circle of mean temperature, there would be a body of surface water which would be sufficiently warmed by the Sun to remain above $4\,°\text{C}$. (Ross seemed to think that the depth of water warmed by solar radiation would depend on how far the radiation penetrated through the water, this being deeper in equatorial and tropical regions; in fact, heat is also redistributed by warm water being mixed downwards.)

At latitudes higher than the circle of mean temperature, water could be cooled to below $4\,°\text{C}$ without sinking down into the deep reservoir: as it could not become *denser* than the reservoir water, it could not sink down through it. (Presumably when water was *at* 4 °C it could sink to the top of the 4 °C reservoir, but the cold conditions at the surface would ensure that this water would be further cooled to below 4 °C.)

(Ross and his contemporaries would have been aware that fresh-water lakes can become stagnant in this way, though most are sufficiently shallow to become thoroughly mixed by wind from time to time.)

Activity 2.3

(a) (i) As discussed in Box 2.2, the stable situation in the ocean is for less-dense water to overlie more-dense water; surface water that has been cooled and made dense will therefore sink to a level determined by its density. (In fact, sinking water often flows down gently sloping surfaces of equal density; for this reason, and others that we don't need to go into here, the distribution of density in the ocean is much more complex than Box 2.2 might imply.)

(ii) The isotherms in Figure 2.17 show that the coldest water in the ocean is that indicated by the dark blue arrows: it sinks from the surface at high southern latitudes and flows northwards below the other water masses. (This coldest water mass is known as Antarctic Bottom Water.) Figure 2.17 shows that, at the start of its journey, this water is colder than 0 °C, but Figure 2.16 contains more precise information because it gives us the freezing temperature of seawater, namely −1.9 °C. We know that seawater increases in density right down to the freezing temperature, so the coldest water sinking from the surface in the ice-bound region of Antarctica must be at a temperature of −1.9 °C (though it quickly mixes with warmer water).

(iii) Because ice is less dense than water, it floats. Once it has formed over a region of ocean it protects the underlying water from further heat loss to the atmosphere. Under present climatic conditions, even the enclosed Arctic Ocean does not freeze down to the sea-floor. (This is in contrast to fresh-water lakes, which can freeze from top to bottom.)

(b) Ross and his contemporaries did not realize that deep water eventually comes to the surface again, particularly in regions where surface water moves apart or 'diverges', notably the Antarctic Divergence shown in Figure 2.17. Divergences and convergences (for example the Antarctic Polar Frontal Zone, or Antarctic Convergence, shown on Figure 2.17) result from the action of wind on surface waters; when the wind pattern causes surface waters to move apart (that is, diverge), deeper water rises to take its place, and when the wind pattern causes surface waters to come together (converge), sinking occurs. Thus, the vertical circulation in the ocean is not simply density-driven convection: the action of wind at the surface also plays a part.

Activity 3.1

(a) Suspension-feeders and deposit-feeders must obtain their nourishment from the organic particles (remains of dead plankton, faecal pellets, etc.) that sink down from above.

(b) Both photographs challenge the assumption that there are no strong currents in the deep sea. The ripple marks in Figure 3.6a can only have been caused by moving water, and the sea-fans in Figure 3.6b seem to have orientated themselves in a particular direction, presumably so as to take advantage of a current carrying food particles (it is also possible that the fish has aligned itself with the current). Also, although it is difficult to see, sediment has been eroded from the sea-bed, exposing rocky outcrops running from left to right.

(c) You may have thought of one or more of the following specific problems:

o Photography can only directly record the animals that live *on* the sediment surface, not those that live beneath it.

o Animals smaller than a certain size will not show up in photographs. The smallest animals that can be seen in the colour original of Figure 3.6b are a centimetre across (the sea-fans are about 30 cm high).

o Individual photographs are 'snapshots' in time. They cannot provide a continuous record, and hence do not tell us anything about, for example, rates of movement of animals. As you will see shortly (Plate 3.2), this problem has, to some extent, been overcome by the use of time-lapse photography. (At present, video cameras are not commonly used in the deep oceans: equipment left for months in such a hostile environment needs to be robust and reliable.)

You may also have thought of a difficulty inherent in photography in deep water — the need for good illumination; even given a powerful light source, there is the problem that light is quite strongly absorbed by seawater and is absorbed and scattered by particles in the water.

Activity 3.2

(a) Given that the density of seawater (ρ_2) is about 1.03×10^3 kg m^{-3}, the density of our 'average' cell (ρ_1) must be $2.2 \times 1.03 \times 10^3$ kg m^{-3}; $\rho_1 - \rho_2$ in Equation 3.1 is therefore $1.03 \times 10^3 \times (2.2 - 1) = 1.03 \times 10^3 \times 1.2 \approx 1.24 \times 10^3$ kg m^{-3}.

Using the other values given:

$$v = \frac{1}{18} \times 9.8 \times \frac{1.24 \times 10^3}{10^{-3}} (10 \times 10^{-6})^2 \, \text{m s}^{-1}$$

$$= 0.67 \times 10^3 \times 10^{-10} \times 10^3 \, \text{m s}^{-1}$$

$$= 0.67 \times 10^{-4} \, \text{m s}^{-1}$$

$$= 6.7 \times 10^{-5} \, \text{m s}^{-1}$$

The settling velocity of our 'typical' cell is therefore about 6.7×10^{-5} m s^{-1}. This is $6.7 \times 10^{-5} \times 24 \times 3\,600 \approx 6$ metres a day, so it would take $4\,000/6 \approx 666$ days — nearly two years — to reach the sea-floor at a depth of $4\,000$ m.

(b) No, it doesn't. Cells sinking at $\approx 7 \times 10^{-5}$ m s^{-1} will be carried 'sideways' at speeds much greater than this. Any correspondence between where a cell leaves the surface and where it ends up on the sea-bed would seem to be most unlikely, and therefore plankton blooms would not be expected to have any detectable effect on the organisms living on the sea-bed directly below.

(c) (i) Reasons you may have thought of are:

1 Planktonic organisms are generally not spherical; many (radiolarians, for example) have spines and protuberances (specially to stop them sinking out of the photic zone) or, in the case of large zooplankton, legs and other organs.

For completeness, we should also mention that for many planktonic organisms our value for ρ_1 would be too high; living planktonic organisms do not consist only of their hard parts (skeletons, etc.), but also contain a variety of low-density substances such as oils and fats. These would take a while to decay away.

2 Stokes's law applies only to a non-turbulent medium. This certainly does not describe the ocean. If we take turbulent motions into account, the trip to the ocean floor would take even longer.

(You may also have thought of the fact that the density of seawater will vary over the $4\,000$ m; this is a valid point, but in fact the factors given in points 1 and 2 have a much larger effect.)

(ii) You could adopt an experimental approach and time how long it takes dead plank-tonic organisms to sink through a given distance in a laboratory tank (it might be tricky to introduce turbulence into your tank in a realistic manner). This is, in fact, how marine biologists initially estimated sinking rates of plankton; the values they obtained were of the order of 5–10 m per day. (Our 'model' gives surprisingly close results, despite the shortcomings identified above.)

(iii) One way or another, a dead plankton cell could well be 'recycled' before it had a chance to sink very far through the ocean. It would be colonized by bacteria, leading in many cases to complete breakdown of its tissue, and the return of its constituents to solution in the water column. Alternatively, it might be consumed by a member of the zooplankton. When excreted as a faecal pellet, the remains of the cell would be part of a much larger object whose sinking rate would be much greater than that of a single cell.

There is one more possibility you may have thought of. We shall come to that shortly!

Activity 4.1

(a) What the map shows is a valley with steep sides (indicated by the closeness of the contours). At its deepest the valley is 200–250 fathoms (370–460 m) deeper than the sea-floor to either side — that is, 1 450–1 500 fathoms (2 650–2 750 m) below sea-level. Within this axial rift valley (for so it is) are a number of topographic highs or hills.

(b) Your sketch should look something like Figure 4.15. If it differs significantly from this, you may be able to spot where you went wrong by comparing the contour values along the cross-section on Figure 4.3c with the depths given on our cross-section (you were not expected to put depths on your sketch). Knowing that magma erupts at spreading ridges to form new ocean floor (Figure 3.2), you may have correctly iden-tified the 'hill' as a volcano. The FAMOUS scientists named it Mount Pluto; the two to the north of the A–B section they named Mount Venus and Mount Jupiter, and the one to the south (less obvious in Figure 4.3c) they named Mount Uranus.

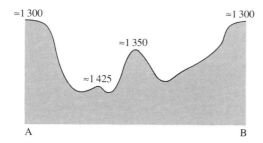

Figure 4.15 Sketch of sea-floor topography along the line A–B on Figure 4.3c. The numbers give approximate depths in fathoms; for example, the top of the volcano must be shallower than a depth of ≈1 350 fathoms.

Activity 4.2

(a) The equation is

$$6CO_2 + 6H_2S + 6O_2 + 6H_2O \xrightarrow{\text{chemical energy}} C_6H_{12}O_6 + 12H^+ + 6SO_4^{2-}$$

from solution in seawater   carbohydrates   to solution in seawater

So we could summarize the difference between chemosynthesis and photosynthesis as follows. In photosynthesis, the Sun's energy is used both to break up the water mol-ecules to release the hydrogen and to combine the hydrogen and the CO_2 (liberating O_2 in the process) to make carbohydrates. In chemosynthesis, it is the energy released by the oxidation ('burning') of H_2S to produce SO_4^{2-} which facilitates the combina-tion of the hydrogen and the CO_2 to make carbohydrates.

(b) One definition of oxidation is *the addition of oxygen and/or the removal of hydro-gen*. The bacteria take H_2S, remove the hydrogen from it and combine the remaining sulphur with oxygen; they have therefore oxidized the hydrogen sulphide to sulphate.

Activity 4.3

(a) Figure 4.16 shows our best-fit mixing line for the Mg^{2+} data in Figure 4.11b.

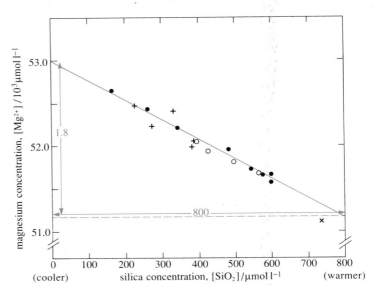

Figure 4.16 Our best-fit mixing line for the Mg^{2+} data in Figure 4.11b.

The intercept on the $[Mg^{2+}]$ axis (B), where $[SiO_2] = 0$ is $\approx (53.0 \times 10^3)\,\mu mol\,l^{-1}$.

The gradient of the line (A) is $-1.8 \times 10^3/800 = -2.25$.

Our equation is therefore

$$[Mg^{2+}] = -2.25[SiO_2] + (53 \times 10^3)\,\mu mol\,l^{-1} \qquad (4.1b)$$

(Don't worry if your values for A and B are slightly different from ours; somewhere between $52.9 \times 10^3\,\mu mol\,l^{-1}$ and $53.2 \times 10^3\,\mu mol\,l^{-1}$ would be acceptable for B; and you may well have obtained a gradient of as low as -2.15 or as high as -2.35.)

(b) Putting $[Mg^{2+}] = 0$ in our new Equation 4.1b

$$0 = -2.25[SiO_2] + (53 \times 10^3)\,\mu mol\,l^{-1}$$

Rearranging,

$$2.25[SiO_2] = (53 \times 10^3)\,\mu mol\,l^{-1}$$

$$[SiO_2] = \frac{53 \times 10^3}{2.25}\,\mu mol\,l^{-1}$$

$$= 23.6 \times 10^3\,\mu mol\,l^{-1}$$

You probably expected that the two calculated $[SiO_2]$ values would be the same, given that they both correspond to undiluted hydrothermal fluid, and in an ideal world they would be. However, the values are within the same 'ballpark', and given the difficulties of sampling and the 'by-eye' method we used for the $[Mg^{2+}]$ plots, the answers are remarkably close.

(c) The average of the two $[SiO_2]$ values is $(23.8 + 23.6) \times 10^3/2$

$$= 23.7 \times 10^3\,\mu mol\,l^{-1}$$

(d) Substituting this average $[SiO_2]$ value of $23.7 \times 10^3\,\mu mol\,l^{-1} = 23\,700\,\mu mol\,l^{-1}$ into Equation 4.2, we get

$$23\,700\,\mu mol\,l^{-1} = 62.5T + 93.8\,\mu mol\,l^{-1}$$

Rearranging,

$$T = \frac{23\,700 - 93.8}{62.5}$$

$$= \frac{23\,606.2}{62.5}$$

$$= 378\,°C$$

The likely temperature of undiluted hydrothermal fluid is therefore $\approx 380\,°C$.

This answer is very close to what the scientists themselves obtained.

Activity 4.4

There isn't a 'right' answer to this question. Points you may have thought of are:

1   The author of the article does not seem to know of the theory that life may have begun with bacterial chemosynthesis in the deep sea (Section 4.4).

2   The phrase 'very major life forms' presumably means 'a large mass of living organisms'; bacteria, though very important in many ways, are not generally referred to as 'major life forms'.

3   The article suggests that because the bacteria were found at depth in granite (rather than in a sedimentary rock) they were unlikely to have originated at the surface. This is questionable: bacteria associated with hydrothermal vents are found covering rocky surfaces and also within cracks in the sea-bed. One possibility would seem to be that hydrothermal circulation within the granite — of fresh water, rather than seawater — could have carried bacteria down into it. (Meteorite impacts generate an enormous amount of heat, so hydrothermal circulation of groundwater is certainly a possibility.)

4   The bacteria *could* originally have been within the meteorite which caused the crater.

Activity 4.5

There is *definitely* no 'right' answer to this! Personally, I agree with Huxley. However, it could be argued that certain aspects of science — particularly modern sciences (quantum theory, for example) — are counter-intuitive and so 'against common sense'. My view is that what matters is the information base used to make the common sense judgement. Rather than rehearse the arguments here, I suggest you read Wolpert's book (see Further reading), but be warned — you may be provoked rather than comforted!

Acknowledgements

The Course Team would like to acknowledge the help and advice of the external assessor for this book, Dr Tony Rice, and his colleagues at the Institute of Oceanographic Sciences Deacon Laboratory. We would also like to thank members of the Open University's *Oceanography* course team.

Grateful acknowledgement is also made to the following sources for permission to reproduce material in this book:

Text

Extract 4.1 Connor, S. (1992), 'Life found deep beneath the earth', *The Independent*, 2 July 1992; *Box 3.1* Huxley's notes: Imperial College Archives, London.

Figures

Figure 2.1 Beebe, W., *Half Mile Down*, New York Zoological Society (1934); *Figure 2.2* New York Zoological Society/The Wildlife Conservation Society; *Figure 2.3* National Maritime Museum; *Figures 2.5a, 3.3* Andrew McIntyre, Lamont–Doherty Geological Observatory, Columbia University; *Figures 2.5b, 2.6b* Dee Breger, Lamont–Doherty Geological Observatory, Columbia University; *Figure 2.6a* Lloyd Burckle, Lamont–Doherty Geological Observatory, Columbia University; *Figures 2.7, 2.19, 2.21* The Natural History Museum; *Figure 3.5 Hornet*, 1871; *Figure 3.7* IOS Deacon Laboratory (NERC); *Figure 3.8* photographs produced by Ian Joint of Plymouth Marine Laboratory for IOS Deacon Laboratory; *Figures 4.1, 4.3, 4.4, 4.5, 4.6* courtesy of the Woods Hole Oceanographic Institution, Woods Hole, Massachusetts; *Figures 4.9, 4.11* Edmond, J. M., Measures, C., McDuff, R. E., Chan, L. H., Collier, R. and Grant, B. (1979), 'Ridge crest hydrothermal activity and the balances of the major and minor elements in the ocean: the Galapagos data', *Earth and Planetary Science Letters*, **46**, Elsevier Science Publications BV.

Colour plates

Plate 2.1 Norman T. Nicoll, Aberdeen; *Plate 3.1* NERC Biogeochemical Flux Study (BOFS); *Plates 3.2, 3.3, 3.4 and 3.5* IOS Deacon Laboratory (NERC); *Plates 4.1 and 4.2* Woods Hole Oceanographic Institution; *Plate 4.3* Craig R. Smith, School of Ocean and Earth Science and Technology, University of Hawaii.

Index

Note   Entries in **bold** are either key terms or are defined in the Science Foundation Course. Page numbers in *italics* refer to figures, tables and colour plates.